Astronomy

is

Heavenly

To SCOTT WRIGHT

HAPPY BIRTHDAY
10/14/2023 ECLIPSE DAY

Astronomy

is

Heavenly

Randy Rhea

Rollalong LLC
2425 Old Monticello Rd
Thomasville, GA 31792
USA
1(229)377-0587

Library of Congress Control Number (LCCN): 2020923279

Second Printing (emended, with Foreword)

Dedication

Chad Boliek

In the distant future, when Chad meets St. Peter, I imagine the conversation will go something like this....

"Chad, my friend, there you are. Well, I'm sure the Boss would agree we can dispense with the credentials, so let's go right to the accommodations phase of check-in. We have a fine group of Presbyterian youth ministers who live over in the section with a fine view of Idaho. Like you, they are fine folks. We also have a nice neighborhood for ministers who voluntarily teach science in middle school. We don't see those often here, but we're an old institution, so there are quite a few. But I suspect where you'll want to live has a beautiful view of Ghost Ranch near Abiquiú in northern New Mexico. It's further from our Sunday meeting place, but it's Joan's favorite spot. What do you think?"

"Well, St. Peter, the latter does sound nice, but wouldn't the word farther have been a better choice than further?"

Chad, my friend, thank you for suggesting better words and ways for telling a story of the Heavens.

Contents

Foreword xiii
Preface xv
1 A Little Science 1
Early Astronomy 1
Epicycles 2
The Copernican Revolution 3
Tycho Brahe 4
The Death of Epicycles 5
Galileo Galilei 6
Isaac Newton 8
Science 9
Big Numbers 11
The Atom 12
Distance Units 14
How Big is the Heavens? 15
Light 16
Magnitude 18
Electromagnetic Waves 19
Mass 19
Determinism 21
Gravity 21
Relativity 22
Gravity and Inertia 23
Einstein's Nobel Prize 24
Weirdness 25
2 The Earth 27
The Third Rock 27
As the World Turns 28
Coordinated Universal Time 29
The Year 30
The Seasons 31
Equinox and Solstice 32
Star Trails and Polaris 32
Precession 34
Ecliptic 34
Artificial Satellites 35
The Clark Belt 37
Observing Artificial Satellites 38

Twinkle, Twinkle, Little Star 39
Meteors 40
Aurora 42
Light Pollution 44
3 Telescopes 47
Optics 47
Binoculars 48
Refracting Telescopes 50
Reflecting Telescopes 52
How to Buy a Telescope 54
Telescope Mounts 55
Celestial Coordinates 56
How to Use a Telescope 57
The Great Telescopes 58
Radio Telescopes 60
Space Telescopes 62
Gravity Waves 66
Low-Hanging Fruit 66
4 The Moon 69
The Moon 69
The Moon's Formation 71
The Tides 71
Observing the Moon 72
The Telescopic Moon 75
Lunar Eclipses 78
Solar Eclipses 80
Observing Solar Eclipses 82
Apollo 84
The Apollo Spacecraft 86
Saturn V 88
5 The Solar System 91
The Solar System 91
Solar System Formation 92
The Sun 93
Sunspots 95
The Ecliptic 97
The Planets 99
Mercury 100
Venus 102
Mars 104
Observing Mars 105
Asteroids 107
Jupiter 109
Observing Jupiter 110
Saturn 111

Observing Saturn 112
Conjunctions 113
Uranus 115
Neptune 116
Pluto... 117
Kuiper Belt and Oort Cloud...................................... 119
Comets.. 120
Voyager... 122
6 Stars.. 123
The Fuel of Stars 123
Stellar Nurseries 124
The Great Orion Nebula 125
Proper Motion... 126
Star Classification 128
Stellar Population 130
Star Names and Catalogs.. 130
Multiple Star Systems... 131
Observing Multiples.. 132
Eclipsing Binaries 133
Variable Stars 134
The Bright Stars 136
Star Death.. 137
Novae... 138
Neutron Stars and Pulsars.. 139
Black Holes.. 140
Star Stuff.. 141
7 The Milky Way 143
The Milky Way 143
Charles Messier... 144
Open Clusters.. 145
Globular Clusters 146
Emission Nebulae 148
Planetary Nebulae... 149
Supernova Remnant 150
Dark Nebulae 152
Other Catalogues.. 153
8 Constellations 155
History... 155
The 88 Constellations... 156
Gemini 159
Ursa Major 161
Leo 163
Ursa Minor 165
Scorpius 166
Hercules... 168

Lyra 169
Sagittarius 171
Cygnus 173
Pegasus 175
Andromeda 176
Cassiopeia 178
Perseus 180
Taurus 181
Orion 183
Auriga 185
The Southern Sky 187

9 Deep Space 193
The Nebulae Mystery 193
Galaxy Types 196
The Local Group 199
Observing Galaxies 200
Hubble Extremely Deep Field 204
Einstein Rings 205
When Worlds Collide 206
Cepheids 207
Expanding Universe 209
The Big Bang 211
Let There Be Light 213
Resistance to the Big Bang 215
Dark Matter 216

10 Aliens 219
The Two Answers 219
UFOs 219
The Drake Equation 222
SETI 223
Active SETI 226
Search for Exoplanets 227
Life on Mars 229
Panspermia 230
Humans on Mars 231
Interstellar Travel 233
That's all Folks 236

11 Resources 237
Books 237
Magazines 238
Clubs 238
Public Planetariums 239
Planisphere 239
Desktop Planetariums 240
App Planetariums 241

Web-based Planetariums 242
General Websites 242
Resellers 243
12 Appendix.. 245
Greek Alphabet 245
Glossary 246
Units, Acronyms, and Abbreviations 250
13 The Images 255
Wikipedia 255
Index... 257

Foreword

"Awesome!" is the expression I frequently hear these days as I stand beside my telescope and listen as a new observer sees for the first time the Andromeda Galaxy stretching from edge to edge in the viewfinder lens.

"Breathtaking!" is another expression I hear as my city-slicker friend glances skyward at the brilliantly lit clear, dark sky above rural, northern New Mexico, seeing something invisible in the glare of modern urban lighting.

"Overwhelming!" is another expression I hear when I try to explain the hundreds of objects one sees (stars. moons, planets, fuzzy smudges) without binoculars or telescopes are all in our own Milky Way galaxy, which happens to be just one of two trillion or so galaxies in the universe.

So there is something in the makeup of the human psyche which responds so enthusiastically to the splendor and vastness of the Heavens. My guess is that this reaction is a universal condition - more prominent in some, more latent in others, and as long as I'm just guessing, I'll go ahead and ask: How did we get that way? Does human DNA somehow compel us to go "gaga" when blessed with a dazzling vision of the night sky? Possibly. Probably.

This, of course, is speculation and not science, but allow me to follow through. On page 141 of this clever and inventive astronomy guide, the author - my long-time friend and fellow sky watcher - offers the section Star Stuff, which I suggest points to the answer.

Put simply, stars, in their super-heated cores and also in their death throes, through the complex process of nuclear fusion, manufacture all the basic elements needed to make other stars and planets and living things. Thus quite literally: we are made of star-stuff. The stars cook up every cell of flesh, bone, brain, and blood in our bodies. The universe is us.

So, like orphans suddenly reunited with long-lost parents, we look up at the sparkling heavens and experience that breath-catching moment of recognition.

Yes! We are here! We are home! We belong! Awesome! Breathtaking! Overwhelming! We are star stuff!

Painters and poets, psalmists and playwrights, physicists and philosophers, and preachers all seek to capture this transcendent cosmic moment. But we don't need to rely on their efforts. What we need, as Randy so aptly puts it, is to step outside on a clear, dark evening, away from city lights, and "look up!" Amen.

Chad Boliek
Sapello, New Mexico

From the safety of Earth, the Heavens are beautiful. A better understanding of the night sky enhances that beauty. Equations and sophisticated science are unneeded. I cannot find the words to describe the contrast of the light from the planets, the stars, and the Milky Way, with the blackness of a moonless and non-light polluted night sky. Many mornings before dawn, as I walked from my observatory back to my cabin, the rocky path through the New Mexico scrub oak was illuminated only by starlight. It's interesting to note that most of that light comes from stars that are too dim to see. Over time, I realized the view of the Heavens with my unaided eyes inspired like the view through the telescope. As when we view the Grand Canyon, our mind is incapable of grasping or remembering the sight. Each time I gaze at the night sky, the sight is as wondrous as the first.

In reality, the Heavens are changing and violent. Some stars are young; some are old. Some are forming; others are dying. Some just fade away: others explode. Some collapse into black holes that would pull you to pieces. Were it not for the atmosphere, we could not withstand the rays and particle storms of our own Sun. But we are protected by distance and by our atmosphere. From a human perspective, change in the Heavens is slow. The Heavens seem unchanging, and the ancients called it the Firmament. But with a better understanding, you can learn to witness change.

The practice of astronomy is ancient. While the atmosphere protects us from many harmful things, it miraculously passes light. Astronomy began with the eyes. Later, astronomers measured the changing positions of the Sun, Moon, planets, and stars using mechanical instruments. Galileo first turned a telescope on the Heavens in 1609. Then Newton showed there was more information in light than met the eyes, so to speak. A scientific revolution was beginning. The English poet Alexander Pope, Newton's contemporary, wrote: "*Nature and nature's laws lay hid in night; God said "Let Newton be" and all was light."*

Through the mid-twentieth century, astronomy depended on light, and that light revealed many secrets. Helium was not discovered on Earth but rather in the light of the Sun. Today the Heavens are probed with telescopes sensitive to light, radio waves, heat, ultraviolet light, and even gravity.

One definition of "faith" by Merriam-Webster is a "firm belief in something for which there is no proof." In that sense, I am a person of unshakable faith in Heaven's creation. There is an order in the universe. Otherwise, science is not possible. If I feel the universe is merely developing through an orderly process of rules that science describes by equations, I must account for the origin of the rules. I will call the creator God. I mean no offense to anyone who doesn't accept the watchmaker God, who believes in a personal God, or who believes in no God at all. Together, we can admire the Heavens.

I write a monthly astronomy column with a reverence for the creation and later assembled those columns into this book. My career was a technical one. While I appreciate the concise mathematical language of equations which describe Newton's law of gravitation, or Einstein's mass/energy relation, equations are not necessary for understanding the Heavens in a way that enhances its beauty in your eyes.

The technology in the modern automobile discourages the shade-tree mechanic. Astronomy today shares that fate. Science and mathematics have progressed to inaccessibility to those without a PhD in astronomy. I don't have a PhD in astronomy, but I've had a passion for astronomy since childhood. If I don't impart your soul with a more beautiful vision of the Heavens with this book, I have failed. But as you read, if you step outside and look up, my task will be an easy one. After all, Astronomy is Heavenly.

1 A Little Science

As the title Astronomy is Heavenly *infers, this book is not written from an advanced scientific perspective. However, adequately covering astronomy requires at least rudimentary science. This first chapter begins with the story of astronomy before it was a science. Then I'll introduce a few scientific terms. Many readers will be familiar with these terms, but a review will help those newer to the subject.*

Early Astronomy

Early astronomy, mythology, and religion were intertwined. There was no light pollution, no sodium-vapor street lights, no billboard lights shining upward, not even a porch light. When night came, there was darkness. An occasional campfire couldn't outshine the Heavens. The view of the Heavens at night inspired wonder, mysticism, and reverence.

The Sun's march through the sky marked the time of day, the Moon marked the months, and the Spring equinox dated the planting. Written history required more sophisticated dating, and calendars developed based on astronomy. Today, the vibrational tick-tock of cesium atoms define time, but astronomy still anchors calendars.

Mankind imagined that the gods resided in the magnificent Heavens. Mystics, soothsayers, and astrologers for royal courts justified their predictions using astronomy. This and intellectual curiosity led to the search for improved data about the motions of the Sun, Moon, planets, and stars. Soon astronomers were using ever more sophisticated tools.

The earliest star catalogs date from about 1200 BC and were written in cuneiform by Babylonians. Greeks considered astronomy a branch of mathematics and, by the 4th -century BC had modeled the motion of the planets and stars on concentric spheres with the Earth in the center. The Egyptians aligned the great pyramids with Thuban, which was at that time the North Star. Polaris is currently our North Star, but it has not been, nor will it always be. I'll return to that subject. Chinese, Mesoamerican, Indian, Native American, Arab, and European cultures all left evidence of early astronomy.

In the 2nd century, Claudius Ptolemy wrote the *Almagest*, a comprehensive book describing and predicting planetary motion. The *Almagest* served as a primary reference for astronomy for 14 centuries. Ptolemy is a Greek name, but he was either Roman or Egyptian, depending on the historian.

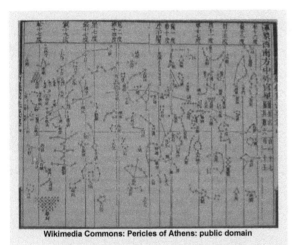
Wikimedia Commons: Pericles of Athens: public domain

About the 10th century, Arabs translated Greek and Indian astronomy. Abd al-Rahman al-Sufi (903 – 986) measured and recorded stellar position, brightness, and color in his *Book of Fixed Stars*. Other Arabs made major contributions to astronomy. Their legacy remains today in a plethora of star and constellation names beginning with the letter *A*. This is a Chinese 1092 AD star map by Su Song.

Epicycles

Ptolemy's model of planetary motion complied with the widespread belief of the day: Earth is the center of the universe. The Moon, Sun, and planets resided on perfectly circular concentric spheres of differing radii, centered on a motionless Earth. The stars resided on the most distant sphere. The idea dated back to Aristotle, a Greek.

But there was a problem. Ptolemy's recorded motions of the planets didn't match the model. Ptolemy expanded on a solution suggested by others hundreds of years before. The answer was a clever one. The Heavenly bodies resided on smaller spheres whose center resided on the original concentric spheres. These smaller circles were referred to as epicycles, epi from Greek for "upon." This model of planetary motion persisted for 14 centuries, but ultimately a more elegant model replaced it.

Later in the book, I'll write about dark matter. Once again, the observed motion in the Heavens suggested something was wrong with our model of matter in the universe. The problem is in the observed spin of galaxies. The current solution proposes an invisible (dark) matter with the gravitational effects to explain the observed spin. The nature of dark matter is unknown, and other than the gravitational effects, evidence for dark matter eludes science. Maybe the observed spin is the result of an unexplained force or an anomaly rather than dark matter. Will dark matter turn out to be a 21st-century idea as contrived as the epicycle, and will it end up on the trash heap of science?

In Europe, during the dark ages from the Roman period until the 12th century, a partial hiatus occurred in astronomy. But European astronomy awoke with a vengeance in what became known as the Copernican revolution.

The Copernican Revolution

In 1543, Nicolaus Copernicus (1473 – 1543) published a book, *De Revoltionibus Orbium Coelestium,* a watershed event in astronomy. In it, he dispelled the notion that the Earth was the center of the universe. He believed that the Sun held that honor and that the planets and the Earth revolved around the Sun. This also meant the Earth was spinning on its axis.

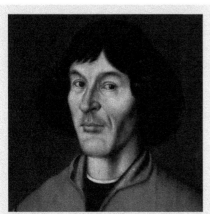

NICOLAUS COPERNICUS
(1473 – 1543) Polish astronomer, mathematician, physician, scholar, governor, diplomat and economist.

Copernicus had drawn his heliocentric conclusion before 1514 and essentially completed his manuscript as early as 1532. Despite encouragement from friends and a Cardinal to publish it, Copernicus was reluctant, possible from fear of religious criticism.

The Greek Aristarchus of Samos wrote of a heliocentric model some 18 centuries earlier, but Copernicus probably independently arrived at his conclusion. In Aristarchus' time, opinion was unwilling to accept that the Earth was spinning and not the center of the universe, and his beliefs drew little attention. The Earth spins? One of my grandsons asked why we don't feel the spin? Imagine you are in a perfectly smooth, moving automobile. Close your eyes. You can't tell the car is moving unless it accelerates or brakes. This difference between constant motion and acceleration was an essential clue for Einstein.

But the next generation of astronomers who followed Copernicus did grasp the concept. For the next century and up to Isaac Newton, astronomers refined the concept mathematically. This major shift in thought became known as the Copernican Revolution.

Tycho Brahe

Tycho Brahe (1546-1601) was a Danish nobleman, astronomer, astrologer, and alchemist. His contribution to astronomy was undoubtedly his passion for precise measurement of the stellar positions and the motion of Heavenly bodies. But having recorded the sudden new star Nova 1572, Brahe also recognized flaws in Aristotle's belief the firmament was unchanging. Brahe offered a theory where Earth is the center of the universe, the Sun, Moon, and stars circle the Earth, and the five planets, known at the time, circled the Sun. This became known as the Tychonic system. It also required epicycles. While inaccurate, many astronomers accepted this system. Tycho Brahe's measurements remained an important source of data for planetary motion theorists to follow.

The Death of Epicycles

Johannes Kepler (1571-1630) was a German astronomer, astrologer, and mathematician. His interest in astronomy developed at an early age as he observed the Great Comet of 1577 and a lunar eclipse. He was also noted for his youthful mathematical ability. He learned about both the Ptolemaic and Copernican systems of planetary motion while in college. He accepted the Copernican system, believing in it from both a mathematical and theological viewpoint. Kepler felt God had created the universe with a plan that was discernable through reason.

In 1594, Kepler accepted a position as a mathematics and astronomy teacher at a Protestant school. He published a book describing the planet's relative distance from the Sun based on spheres enclosing a solid three-dimensional polyhedral of increasing order. The work established him as a skilled astronomer.

Kepler became aware of Tycho Brahe's work, and after lengthy negotiations, Kepler began to work for Brahe in Prague in 1600, giving Kepler access to Brahe's motional data. A year later, Brahe unexpectedly died, and Kepler became his successor as the mathematician to Emperor Rudolf II. For the next decade, Kepler published on astronomy, optics, and the physiology of the human eye. During this time, he also struggled with prevailing political turmoil and family health issues.

In 1617, 1620, and 1621, he published his three-volume textbook *Epitome Astronomiae Copernicanae*. Even though it contained the now famous three laws of planetary motion, astronomers did not initially accept his theories. However, after his death, the textbook became widely used and accepted. Johannes Kepler's three laws of planetary motion are

(1) The orbit of a planet is an ellipse with the Sun at one focus.

(2) A line segment joining a planet and the Sun sweeps out equal areas during equal intervals of time.

(3) The square of the orbital period of a planet is directly proportional to the cube of the semi-major axis.

Heliocentricity and elliptical rather than circular orbits dissolved the need for epicycles, but Kepler's concepts were slow to be accepted. Many continued to accept either the Copernican or the Tychonic system.

As is commonly the case with science, Kepler's laws did not consider more subtle factors. For example, they do not consider the gravitational effect of the planets on each other. Because the Sun is far more massive than the planets, the needed correction is minor but real. I'll bring this correction up again. Kepler's laws also do not include the effects of Einstein's theory of General Relativity. The differences this causes in planetary motion later became a test of Einstein's theory.

Galileo Galilei

Galileo Galilei (1564 – 1642) was born in Pisa, Italy, to a composer and lute player. Galileo also became an accomplished lute player. Like many other early astronomers, Galileo's ties to faith were strong. He considered becoming a priest but choose to study medicine. While studying at the University of Pisa, he noticed a chandelier's swing and soon experimented with pendulums. A shift to the study of mathematics followed.

Galileo was a Copernican, although he doubted Kepler's elliptical orbits. Galileo is credited with being the first to turn a telescope on the Heavens in 1609. He soon discovered Jupiter had a discernable disk and was orbited by four moons. Closer moons circled faster. Here was evidence of a system of orbits around a body other than the Earth, an example that the Earth is not the center of everything. He also discovered that Venus experienced all phases like the Moon, including full. The Ptolemaic model displays only crescent phases, while the Copernican model displays all phases.

Galileo wrote passionately about his heliocentric views. Copernicus had avoided scorn, but Galileo would not. Objections arose not only for religious reasons but also for vindictive reasons as well. Previous Cardinals and Popes had shown interest in Copernicus and Galileo's heliocentric theories. They not only failed to condemn these theories but even encouraged publication.

Wikimedia Commons: Justus Sustermans: public domain
GALILEO GALILEI
(1564 – 1642) Italian engineer, astronomer, and physicist.

However, Galileo had made a fervent adversary with the Jesuit scholar Mario Guiducci by writing an article disclaiming Guiducci's theories on comets. In that article, Galileo insulted and alienated the Jesuits. He further alienated scholars by implying he invented the telescope. Galileo also received little support from astronomers who still accepted the Tychonic system.

By 1615, Galileo's writings reached the Roman Inquisition, a tribunal system established by the Catholic Church to prosecute persons responsible for heresy. The tribunal commuted a prison sentence to house arrest, and Galileo would no longer be allowed to publish his theories. But the swelling of ideas during the Scientific Revolution could not be diminished by the Inquisition.

Isaac Newton

Isaac Newton (1643 – 1727) was born a small premature child in an English hamlet on Christmas Day, 1642, by the Julian calendar used at the time, or January 4, 1643, by the current Gregorian calendar. His father, also named Isaac Newton, died three months before his son's birth. When he was three, Newton's mother remarried and left Newton in his maternal grandmother's care. Newton received a classical education in Greek, Latin, and mathematics at The King's School in Grantham, a school with roots traceable to 1329. When Newton was 17, his mother was widowed for the second time and removed him from school to have him farm. Newton hated farming, and the schoolmaster convinced Newton's mother to let him return. He was the top-ranked student and was soon admitted to Trinity College, Cambridge. He worked his way through college until receiving a scholarship. In August of 1665, Trinity College was temporarily closed due to the Great Plague. While he had been an average student at Trinity, two years of private study at home led to his groundbreaking developments in calculus, optics, and gravitation.

A brilliant mathematician, Newton created differential calculus and other mathematics. He found a mathematical solution to Kepler's laws of planetary motion, accurately described the nature of color, and showed that a rainbow could be re-assembled into white light with a prism. He built the first practical reflecting telescope, the form great telescopes use today to probe the universe. NASA used his laws of gravitation and motion

Wikimedia Commons: Godfrey Kneller: public domain

ISAAC NEWTON

(1564 – 1642) English mathematician, astronomer, physicist, and theologian. Author of Principia.

to place men on the Moon. His manuscript *Principia* was published in 1687 and established him as the most extraordinary mind of the scientific revolution, an honor Newton undisputedly held until Einstein modified Newton's laws for fantastic speeds. Newton finally vindicated Kepler, whose theories became universally accepted.

Newton was 46 in 1689 when he sat for the leading portrait painter in England, Godfrey Kneller. Newton lived during his fame but was modest. He wrote, *"I do not know what I may appear to the world, but to myself I seem to have been only like a boy playing on the sea-shore, and diverting myself in now and then finding a smoother pebble or a prettier shell than ordinary, whilst the great ocean of truth lay all undiscovered before me."*

Science

The Scientific Revolution and the Age of Enlightenment are siblings. The Scientific Revolution marked unparalleled advancements in astronomy, mathematics, physics, chemistry, and biology. Perhaps it began with Copernicus' publication in 1543 of *De Revoltionibus Orbium Coelestium,* which dispelled an Earth-centric system of planetary motion. Maybe the Scientific Revolution ended in 1687 with the publication by Newton of *Principia,* which included his laws of motion and gravity.

Following the Scientific Revolution was the younger sibling, the Age of Enlightenment. Perhaps it began with *Principia.* During the Age of Enlightenment, the senses and reason were believed to be the source of knowledge rather than revelation. Books, journals, Masonic lodges, and scientific societies shared the new knowledge. Political ideals included liberty, tolerance, constitutional government, and separation of Church and state. From an American perspective, it was the backdrop of independence for the Colonies. The scientific method won philosophers' hearts and minds, rather than mysticism, the Catholic Church's dogma, and the King. The French philosopher Denis Diderot (1713 – 1784) wrote, *"Men will never be free until the last king is strangled with the entrails of the last priest."*

So, what is science? From Latin, science means knowledge. A definition by Webster is *"knowledge as distinguished from ignorance or misunderstanding."* I think this definition is lacking. Newton's laws on planetary motion were not precise because they didn't consider Einstein's General Relativity. They were a misunderstanding. Does that mean Newton wasn't a scientist?

I would argue that science is more a method than an answer. While scientific knowledge is continually changing, the method has changed little since the Scientific Revolution. The basics of the method are:

(1) Start with a question and make observations.
(2) Create a hypothesis that explains the observation.
(3) Test the hypothesis.
(4) Modify the hypothesis if necessary.
(5) Make a prediction with the hypothesis.

If you don't make it through (5), you've got to start over. The result of the method is knowledge. Science creates knowledge; it's not merely the body of knowledge. To successfully practice science requires curiosity and the ability to ask the right questions, followed by honesty and a willingness to be wrong. Science is subjective because humans conduct it. It's objective because others must repeat the results.

It's tempting to regard science as pure logic and reason. It's not. The 1933 co-recipient of the Nobel Prize in Physics was Paul Dirac. His contributions to quantum theory are still legion. His strange personality was also legion. Dirac once stated to a student that his fundamental belief was that

Wikimedia Commons: Nobel Foundation: public domain

PAUL DIRAC
(1902 – 1984) English theoretical physicist and Nobel laureate

beautiful equations should express nature's laws. The beautiful Dirac equation was named after him, and the operative word here was beauty. He wrote and often commented on the theme of beauty in science.

Beauty in science is perhaps easier to define than beauty in art. For one, the solution should be elegant. Epicycles were not elegant. They were contrived to make a flawed theory fit the data. Kepler's elliptical orbits were perhaps not as elegant as the Greek perfect circle, but they were undoubtedly better than epicycles. Another example of beauty in science is simplicity. Einstein's famous equation, $E=mc^2$, simply expresses that matter and energy are essentially the same. Finally, science and aesthetic beauty are expressed in symmetry, as exemplified in architecture, music, palm leaves, and many animal forms. For Dirac, every particle must have an antiparticle, and the electron must have a positron, ideas others ultimately confirmed.

Dirac believed the true measure of a theory was its beauty. Beauty was more important than the theory fitting all the data. Be patient; the data will come around to a beautiful theory. As we will see, Einstein would have avoided a minor embarrassment later in his career if he had embraced this dictum.

Big Numbers

The human mind simply can't grasp the scale of the known universe. Instruments now exist to see the edge of the universe and measure that distance with some accuracy. But knowing the numbers isn't enough to truly grasp the significance. Driving to town, from city to city, or even traveling around the globe does not prepare us to comprehend the universe's scale. The human mind can't do it.

Even though we can't grasp the universe's scale, we can try by learning about big numbers. The average distance to the Moon is 238,856 miles. The orbit isn't circular, so the distance varies about ten percent. The distance to the Sun is about 92,956,000 miles. The distance to the nearest star, Proxima Centauri, is about 24,950,000,000,000 miles.

The distance to our sister galaxy, Andromeda, is 14,930,000,000,000,000,000 miles. Are you tired of counting zeros? I hate to bear bad news about this counting-zeros problem, but the Andromeda galaxy is still in our celestial neighborhood.

DECIMAL	SCIENTIFIC
4	4×10^0
.00000000002	2×10^{-11}
3,000,000,000	3×10^9
50	5×10^1

Science offers two solutions to this big-number problem. The first is called scientific notation. Consider the distance to the Andromeda galaxy. Write 1.439 and then count the number of digits right of the decimal point. It's nineteen digits. So, in scientific notation, it's 1.439×10^{19} miles. A calculator displays it as 1.439E19. The table shows some examples. You can see it doesn't help with regular numbers, but it's great for big and small numbers.

The numbers may be too big to grasp, but at least someone else is counting the zeros for you. Scientific notation is pretty handy for big numbers. The 19 is called the exponent. For example, what is three million times two billion? That is 3×10^6 times 2×10^9. You just multiply 3 x 2 and add the exponents, so it's 6×10^{15}.

PREFIX	NUMBER	SCIENTIFIC
nano	0.000000001	1×10^{-9}
micro	0.000001	1×10^{-6}
milli	0.001	1×10^{-3}
centi	0.01	1×10^{-2}
kilo	1,000	1×10^3
mega	1,000,000	1×10^6
giga	1,000,000,000	1×10^9

It's a convenient way to keep up with the zeros in large numbers. Before scientific calculators, scientific notation was the only practical way to deal with big and small numbers on a slide rule. Science also uses scientific notation as a basis for prefixes to decrease or increase the size of units. For example, a kilometer is 1000 meters, and 1/1000th of a second is a millisecond.

The Atom

The word atom is derived from the Greek atomos, meaning uncuttable. The idea dates long before Newton, at least as far back as 440 BC, by the Greek philosopher Democritus (c.460 BC – c.370 BC). The atom is the smallest unit of matter because an atom is the smallest unit that retains each element's unique chemical property. One hundred fifty years after Newton, John Dalton showed how elements combine in ways suggesting atoms. Amazing - wow - science confirmed the smallest unit of matter.

But wait - 50 years later, Ernest Rutherford discovered the nucleus of atoms was composed of smaller units of protons and neutrons. Wait again - the current status of particle science is called the standard model of elementary particles. This model posits that the classic proton consists of two up quarks, one down quark, and gluons, while the neutron consists of two down quarks, one up quark, and gluons. The particles of the standard model are the only particles to have been experimentally observed and confirmed. They constitute baryonic matter, all the known matter of the universe.

The standard model is the culmination of modern research on the atom and matter. However, the model does not explain gravity, dark matter, or dark energy (I will write about darkness later). Also, the model is not elegant or beautiful in that it utilizes multiple parameters that appear arbitrary and unrelated.

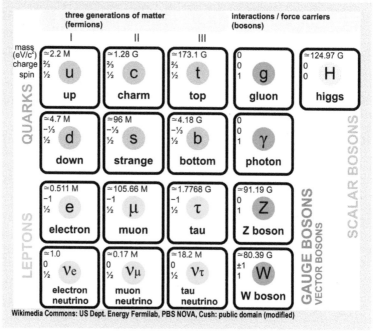

Wikimedia Commons: US Dept. Energy Fermilab, PBS NOVA, Cush: public domain (modified)

The finding in 2012 of the predicted Higgs boson particle left some scientists so enamored they called it the "God particle," and scientists currently seek the so-called "theory of everything." No model of matter yet devised has withstood the test of time as being complete. Perhaps science should take a lesson in Newton's humility and remember each answered question has always spawned new questions. The depth of the atom inward may be as unknowable as the marvel of God's universe outward.

Distance Units

The second solution science offers for the counting zeros problem is to define new units of distance. The distance from the Earth to the Sun is called the Astronomical Unit, or the au. Although the distance varies, as a standard, it's defined as 92.956 million miles or 9.2956×10^7 miles for the au. Astronomers use this unit for distances within the Solar system. For example, the average distance from the Sun to Mercury is 0.387 au, to Venus is 0.723 au, to Earth is one au, and to Mars is 1.523 au.

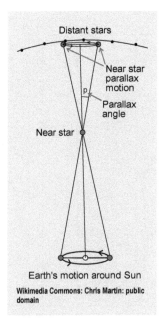

Distant stars

Near star parallax motion

p

Parallax angle

Near star

Earth's motion around Sun

The next defined unit of distance is the parsec. The story about a parsec is a little more involved. Did you know you are a math wizard? No, you are, and I don't mean adding, subtracting, multiplying, and dividing. I mean trigonometry and analytic geometry. If no one is watching, put up a finger, close one eye, and then the other. Notice your finger shifts relative to the background. This is parallax. Your brain takes the view from each eye, computes the shift using trig, and then tells you your finger is 18 inches away. Fortunately, your brain also puts the two fingers back together. It's accurate. After looking at a glass on the table, you can even close your eyes, reach out, and pick up the glass.

Perhaps you've watched an infant in his crib reaching up to the mobile and looking intently. He is learning trig. At a young age, babies learn to reach for their glass on the highchair tray. OK, so maybe they haven't mastered it yet and knock over the glass. Thank heavens for the Sippy cup. According to Wikipedia, the Sippy cup was invented in 1981 by Richard Belanger....but I digress.

Stars are farther than your finger, so the parallax is very small. However, by 1806, Giuseppe Calandrelli found parallax in the star Alpha Lyrae. Because the stars are far away, a large separation is needed, such as two extreme points in the Earth's orbit around the Sun. Even so, the shift is small.

This idea of using the Earth's orbit around the Sun to create widely separated viewpoints for parallax led to the parsec unit of distance. With a separation of one au, one parsec's distance results in an angular shift one arc-second shift. One arc-second is 1/3600 of a degree. One parsec is 19 trillion miles or 1.9×10^{13} miles. Professional astronomers commonly use the parsec.

A more common unit of vast distance in popular astronomy is the light-year, abbreviated ly. The light-year is not a unit of time; it's a unit of distance. It's the distance light travels in 365.25 days. Light is fast, so it travels a long way in a year. If a light beam followed the Earth's curvature, it would circle the Earth seven times in one second. A light-year equals 5.8786×10^{12} miles. The nearest star, Proxima Centauri, is 4.244 light-years. So, we can now conveniently write big numbers, but they're still unimaginable.

How Big is the Heavens?

Let's start close to home with the Moon. Four hundred years before the birth of Christ, the Greek Aristarchus used parallax observations from two cities of known separation to estimate the distance to the Moon. Two hundred years later, Hipparchus used parallax during a Lunar eclipse and came up with a reasonably accurate distance to the Moon. Apollo 11, 14, and 15 astronauts left mirrors on the Moon. Laser light bouncing off these mirrors continues to measure the distance. As it orbits Earth, the Moon is spiraling away from us about 1.5 inches a year. I guess if we're going back, we'd better hurry.

For the closest stars, the parallax shift is about the diameter of a quarter three miles away. Further complicating the parallax measurement of stars is our turbulent atmosphere, which acts like a lens and bends and blurs the light. So Earth-bound measurement accuracy limits the range to approximately 300 ly. In astronomical terms, that's close, real close. In 1989, the European Space Agency (ESA) launched the satellite Hipparchus above the atmosphere to measure more distant stars. Its accurate measurement range was about 100,000 stars out to 1600 ly. The ESA more sophisticated Gaia satellite replaced the no longer operating Hipparchus. Even so, parallax is only valid for measuring distance in our neighborhood of the universe.

So how far are the stars? The closest star is Proxima Centauri, and it's 4.2 ly. Traveling at the fastest speed man has ever traveled (Apollo 10 – 24,816 mph), it would take 115,000 years to reach Proxima Centauri. It's viewable only in the Southern Hemisphere. The closest star bright enough to see from the Northern Hemisphere is Sirius, about twice as far as Proxima Centauri.

Measuring distance beyond the nearest stars is less direct. I'll write about that in a later chapter. But for now, without explanation, the distance to the nearest large galaxy, Andromeda, is 2.5 million ly, and the distance to the furthest known galaxy is 13.3 billion ly or 7.8×10^{22} miles. I'm glad I don't need to count those zeros.

Light

Light is a wonderful gift that unlocks the secrets of the Heavens. As I stated in the Preface, the atmosphere shields us from the harmful rays of the Sun, but it passes visible light, and there is more to that light than meets the eyes. Joseph Ritter von Fraunhofer (1787 – 1826) was a German physicist and optical glassmaker. He invented the spectroscope, an instrument for analyzing light. This image is a spectrograph image of light from the Sun. Ultraviolet is

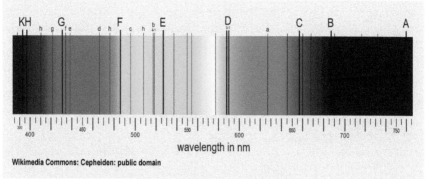

Wikimedia Commons: Cepheiden: public domain

on the left, and infrared is on the right. Elements in the Sun's atmosphere impose dark lines at specific wavelengths in the solar spectrum. Each element creates multiple lines at unique wavelengths, thus leaving a fingerprint of the element.

The second most abundant element in the universe is helium, that crazy stuff that makes a balloon float in the air and makes you talk like Donald Duck when you inhale it. Helium is rare in our atmosphere because it's so energetic that it moves about so fast it can escape our atmosphere.

About the time of the American Civil War, scientists began systematically recording the spectrums of all the chemical elements. In 1868, the French astronomer Jules Janssen (1824 – 1907) noticed a yellow spectral line in sunlight during an eclipse. Later that same year, an English astronomer Norman Lockyer (1836 – 1920), observed the same line, but he recognized it for what it was. Sunlight had lines of an element not yet found on Earth. It was named helium, after the Greek god of the Sun. It would be confirmed on Earth some 27 years later.

Using spectroscopes attached to telescopes, scientists can identify the elements in every object that shines light on Earth, including the Sun, other planet's atmospheres, the stars, galaxies, and even clouds of dark gas that the light shines through. When an object approaches or recedes from us, the frequencies of the spectral lines shift; a phenomenon called Doppler shift. From this, we learn the velocity of objects relative to us. That is how Edwin Hubble first measured the universe's expansion. Light provides a veritable treasure trove of information about our universe. When God gave us light, he not only illuminated and warmed us, he gave us a tool to illuminate our minds. If you seek proof of God, just open your eyes. You'll see the light.

Magnitude

Magnitude is a measure of brightness for celestial objects. Apparent magnitude is the brightness observed from the Earth. Absolute magnitude is the magnitude the object would have if viewed from a distance of ten parsecs. Of course, a star viewed from a greater distance would be dimmer. So, absolute magnitude is a measure of the brightness at a standard distance. For example, a faint star might be a bright star that is further away. In stellar classification, the absolute magnitude is more important. The visual or apparent magnitude is what we see with our eyes. Unless specified otherwise, magnitude in this book refers to the apparent magnitude we see from Earth.

Magnitude is measured on a reverse logarithmic scale, so brighter stars have smaller magnitudes. Each larger number is 2.514 times dimmer than the smaller. It's a Greek tradition formalized in 1856. The relatively stable star Vega was assigned magnitude 0.0. That means Sirius, which is brighter than Vega, is magnitude -1.4. The dimmest stars we can see in non-light polluted skies is about six. The magnitude of the brightest planet, Venus, is -2.7, and the magnitude of the Sun is -26.74. The absolute magnitude of the Sun is 4.8, meaning it's of average brightness. Given in the table are the quantity of visible stars greater than a given magnitude, according to the US National Solar Observatory. The quantity of stars you can see is countable at just over 7,000. But they aren't all visible at any given time. Also, unless you are on the equator, you can't see both northern and southern stars.

MAG	QUAN
0	4
1	15
2	48
3	171
4	513
5	1602
6	4800

Electromagnetic Waves

Light is a particular range of wavelengths of electromagnetic waves. Electromagnetic waves are a combination of electric fields (think voltage and batteries) and magnetic fields. They don't require a medium to travel in like sound, which requires a gas, liquid, or solid. In a vacuum, electromagnetic waves travel at the speed of light. Radio waves, heat, light, UV rays, and X-rays are all electromagnetic waves.

James Clerk Maxwell (1831 – 1879) was a Scottish scientist and mathematician. In Edinburgh, he was born to a father of comfortable means and a 40-year old mother who homeschooled him. Maxwell published his theory of electromagnetic radiation in 1865. Scientists believed that light traveled in a medium called the ether, but Maxwell dispelled the need for a medium. His theory also

Wikimedia Commons: George Stodard: public domain
JAMES CLERK MAXWELL
(1831 – 1879) Scottish scientist and mathematician. Author of Maxwell's equations.

predicted radio waves before their discovery. Maxwell's work was indeed a watershed moment in science. Einstein described Maxwell's contributions as the *"most profound and the most fruitful that physics has experienced since the time of Newton."*

Mass

I'll never forget a dramatic demonstration in my college Physics 101 class. A bowling ball was suspended from the ceiling of a large, stadium-style lecture hall. The professor asked a volunteer student to stand with the back of his head against the blackboard. The professor pulled the ball back to the student's nose and let go. The ball swung like a

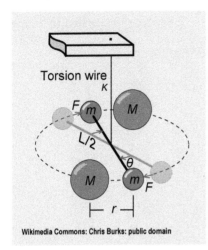

Torsion wire
K

Wikimedia Commons: Chris Burks: public domain

pendulum out away from the student some 15 feet, stopped, and began its threatening swing back. As the ball approached, the student ducked. Elementary physics says it would have stopped right at his nose. But the student's faith in physics was weaker than his intuitive understanding of inertia and the concern for his nose. I suppose there is also the suspicion that the professor gave the ball a slight push. There were many fascinating demonstrations in that class, and I developed a passion for physics.

Mass is a fundamental property of a physical body. Mass is different than weight. Consider that fourteen-pound bowling ball. Take it to the Moon, and it's the same ball with the same mass, but it weighs only 2.3 pounds.

Nevertheless, the inertia of that bowling ball is the same on Earth and the Moon. Traveling at the same speed, whether it hit you on the Earth or the Moon, the ball would have the same impact. It takes the same force to start or stop it rolling on both worlds.

Mass attracts mass. The attraction of our body to the Earth gives us weight. But is there a way to measure this force independent of the Earth? The British scientist Henry Cavendish (1731 – 1810), who also discovered hydrogen, did it and published the result in 1798. He made careful and precise measurements, and his result was accurate.

He used a device called a torsion balance shown in the figure. Two-inch diameter 1.61-pound lead spheres are placed on each end of a six-foot wooden rod, suspended from above with a wire. Twisting the wire requires very little force. Two larger twelve-inch diameter 348-pound lead balls are then placed beside the smaller balls causing the wire to twist. Measuring the oscillation period of the rod set to swinging without the larger balls present allowed computation of the force required to twist the wire.

Determinism

By 1814, the Enlightenment's idea that reason was the true source of knowledge, along with all the masterful accomplishments of science, led the great French mathematician, astronomer, and philosopher Pierre Simon Laplace (1749 - 1827) to write:

We may regard the present state of the universe as the effect of its past and the cause of its future. An intellect which at a certain moment would know all forces that set nature in motion, and all positions of all items of which nature is composed, if this intellect were also vast enough to submit these data to analysis, it would embrace in a single formula the movements of the greatest bodies of the universe and those of the tiniest atom; for such an intellect nothing would be uncertain, and the future just like the past would be present before its eyes.

Laplace said that given enough data and a big enough computer, the future is predictable. We can't change it. There is no free will.

In the mid-1900s, simulations of the weather and other systems using analog and later digital computers showed that tiny changes in the initial data significantly affected the outcome. One scientist, writing about this, titled his paper *"Does the flap of a butterfly's wing in Brazil set off a tornado in Texas?"* The study of this problem is called chaos theory. However, is the prediction failure fundamental or just a measure of current capability? The answer is coming in a few more pages.

Gravity

According to Newton, mass attracts mass. The force is proportional to the product of the masses; in other words, the greater the masses, the greater the force. The Earth is massive, and our attraction to it is strong. A simple bathroom scale is the depressing evidence of our mass. This force is called gravity.

Gravity is one of the four fundamental forces of nature. A second force is electromagnetic. Radio and light result from this force. These first two forces work at humanly perceivable distances. A third force is the strong nuclear force, which is much stronger than the first two forces, but it only functions at the subatomic range. It holds matter together. The fourth force is the weak nuclear force. It's responsible for radioactive decay, and it also operates only at the subatomic range.

Newton created a simple equation to describe gravity as a force. Newton never claimed an apple hit him on the head, but he did say a falling apple gave him the notion of gravity. His equation works fine for everyday mechanics. It predicts the force is proportional to the product of two masses and decreases with the distance squared. Both the electromagnetic and gravitational forces decrease with the square of distance because a sphere's area increases with the radius squared. The spread over a greater area weakens the light. Step twice as far back from a lightbulb, and the resulting illumination on a surface is four times dimmer.

ALBERT EINSTEIN
(1879 – 1955) Official portrait for the 1921 Nobel Prize in Physics

Relativity

Einstein developed two theories of relativity. The first, published in 1905, was the Special Theory of Relativity. It studied motion and light under the special condition that any motion was constant and didn't include acceleration. Einstein's insight often came from what he called gedankenexperiment, German for thought experiments. In the case of Special Relativity, he imagined a lightning strike in front of a moving train, just when a viewer of the strike on the train passes a stationary viewer at a station. Because Einstein believed the speed of light to be finite and absolute, the viewer on the train, traveling toward the strike, would see the strike slightly before the stationary viewer. They would see the strike at different "times." What? Did the strike not occur "when" it occurred? Simultaneous has no meaning. Einstein realized this meant time is relative to motion, and there is no such thing as absolute time. The math was simple algebra, but when extended naturally to the concept of mass and length, they were relative also. Not even the measurement of something as straightforward as length was absolute but was relative to motion. This set science on its head.

Gravity and Inertia

Einstein next set to work on a theory that allowed for acceleration. It would be called the General Theory of Relativity. Using another gedankenexperiment, he imagined a person inside an enclosed box. If that box were sitting on the Earth, the person would "feel" gravity as their weight. Now imagine the box is in deep space with no massive Earth to pull "down." The person in the box would be weightless and drift about in the box. Now imagine a cable is attached to the box and pulls the box at a constant rate of acceleration. If the rate happened to be 32 feet per second faster for each second passed (the acceleration rate of gravity on Earth), the person in the box would "feel" like he was standing in a box on the Earth. Einstein realized gravity and acceleration were the same.

Unlike the Special Theory, the math to expresses this wasn't straightforward algebra. Einstein struggled with the math for years and finally had to get help from an old friend and mathematician. The required math involved a late development in mathematics called tensors. Einstein published his General Theory in 1915.

His General Theory of Relativity states that gravity isn't a force. Instead, mass warps space. Imagine a flat sheet of balloon rubber. Place a marble on the sheet, and the marble makes a depression. Place another marble on the sheet, and they accelerate toward each other. It seems like a force, and it's conveniently still referred to as a force.

Einstein's Nobel Prize

Einstein's gedankenexperiment doesn't quite fit the rules of science. Einstein hadn't attempted to fit theory to physical experiments. His approach was akin to philosophy. Aristotle's philosophy led to the common-sense idea that heavy objects fall faster than light objects. In 1971, while standing on the lunar surface, astronaut David Scott dropped a hammer and a feather. They struck the surface at the same time. On Earth, air resistance to motion slows a lightweight feather. Philosophy lacks the check and balance of experimental proof. Einstein backed up his insights with mathematical descriptions, but while math and science are cousins, they aren't sisters.

Even though Einstein's relativity theories were the most profound works in science since Newton and Maxwell, he never received the Noble Prize for either theory. The reasons are several: some are somewhat justifiable, and others remind us humans prosecute science.

The General Theory's math was difficult for non-specialists, and the consequences of the theory were profound and unsettling to science. The theories received experimental confirmation only well after their publication. At the time, one member of the Nobel committee was jealous of Einstein's success, was antisemitic, and probably didn't understand the General Theory. He derailed awarding Einstein the Prize more than once. In the end, the Nobel committee realized not awarding the Prize to Einstein would ultimately be embarrassing for the Prize. As a compromise, Einstein was awarded the Nobel Prize in 1921 for his 1905 work in photoelectricity. Ironically, had the Prize for photo electricity been awarded to someone else, it would probably have been to his antagonist, who, therefore, inadvertently derailed his own Prize.

Einstein was touring Japan at the time, and he didn't attend the Nobel banquet. He later gave a Nobel acceptance lecture of sorts to the Nordic Assembly of Naturalists at Gothenburg. In that lecture, Einstein got in the last word. He didn't speak about the photoelectric effect but instead his General Theory of Relativity.

Einstein spent the last few decades of his life searching for an overall theory to unify gravity and electromagnetism. He failed, and during his search, he became somewhat isolated from the physics community. Later, scientists identified the strong and weak forces. Now that these four fundamental sources are known, physicists attempt to unify them in a so-called Theory of Everything. Like Einstein, so far, they have failed.

Weirdness

At the turn of the 20th century, scientists began to realize that reality is weird. Evidence of this first appeared in the 19th century. By 1900, Max Planck (1858 – 1947) began to define the weirdness mathematically and formally. Albert Einstein's Nobel Prize was for showing that light comes in individual bits (quantized). Light behaves both like a particle and a wave, but even as a wave, at only specific colors. Einstein asked, *"is it possible to combine energy quanta and the wave principles of radiation? Appearances are against it, but the Almighty – it seems – managed the trick."*

All of this happens at atomic sizes. Larger objects behave classically. That classic view is intuitive in human experience, and what Newton described by using what is now high-school mathematics. By the 1920s, this new science about small things was called quantum physics, or quantum mechanics.

In this model, nothing is certain. It's impossible to know how fast an electron is traveling and where it's at the same time. Only the probability of something is predictable. Richard Feynman (1918 – 1988) wrote that quantum mechanics deals with *"nature as She is – absurd."* Einstein was initially skeptical of quantum mechanics, and asserted *"He does not play dice."* Niels Bohr (1885 – 1962), another Nobel Prize-winning physicist and lifelong friend and sparring partner, advised Einstein to *"stop telling God what to do."* It turned out He does play dice. The creation includes everything, so it includes dice. Another Einstein reflection was, *"the more success the quantum theory enjoys, the sillier it looks."*

Quantum mechanics tells us it's theoretically impossible to measure a system precisely enough to set up the initial conditions necessary for a computer simulation of the future. Scientific determinism was an exercise in scientific optimism. There is free will, and we can influence the future.

Quantum mechanics is required to rigorously describe what science believes about the Heavens. However, the mathematics of quantum mechanics, and even the terminology, is inaccessible to non-specialists. I'll bring up quantum mechanics occasionally, but for the most part, I'll avoid the weirdness and deal with the beauty of the night skies. After all, Astronomy is Heavenly.

2 The Earth

The Earth might seem an unusual chapter in an astronomy book, but the Earth is central to how we view the Heavens. The Earth spins, circles the Sun, is tilted, it precesses like a top, and we peer through its atmosphere. These all affect our view of the Heavens.

The Third Rock

The four planets closest to the Sun: Mercury, Venus, Earth, and Mars, all have rocky surfaces. The more distant planets are gaseous. Earth, of course, is the third rock from the Sun. Well, at least 29% of the surface is rock or dirt.

Eratosthenes (276 BC – 194 BC) was a Greek mathematician, astronomer, poet, music theorist, and chief librarian at the Great Library of Alexandria. Around 240 BC, he was the first to calculate the Earth's circumference, doing it without leaving home. Eratosthenes knew that the Sun was directly overhead at noon on the summer solstice in Aswan, Egypt. He measured the length of the shadow of a vertical rod in Alexandria and calculated the shadow's angle to be about 7°. This is approximately 1/50th of a circle, so he multiplied the distance to Aswan by 50. His result was pretty close. I guess he didn't think the Earth is flat.

As noted in the first chapter, in 1798, Henry Cavendish measured the gravitational constant of mass. From that, he could calculate the mass of the Earth, and knowing the diameter, he calculated the average density of Earth. The density was higher than water or rock, suggesting a metallic core for the Earth.

It turns out, the third rock from the Sun has a solid iron-nickel core surrounded by a molten metallic core. Convection currents create motion in the molten iron core,

Wikimedia Commons: Apollo 17 crew: public domain

which produces Earth's magnetic field. Like the atmosphere, the magnetic field also protects us from charged particles emanating from the Sun.

The axis of the rotating currents in the iron is not aligned precisely with the Earth's rotational axis; it's currently off by about 11°, which causes magnetic deviation. The pole of that giant magnet is presently in northern Canada rather than the north geographic pole. The magnetic field's strength and pole position are not constant, but the position changes slowly enough to allow valid magnetic deviation data.

The continents float and move around on the molten magma in an idea referred to as plate tectonics. The continents are not where they have always been. Not only does the magnetic pole move, but over hundreds of thousands of years, it flips polarity. The south pole of the magnet is currently in northern Canada. The flipping of the magnet leaves a record in rock, which helps to study tectonic plate shift. So much for the idea of terra firma.

As the World Turns

The chapter titled Solar System describes the formation of the Earth and Solar system. For now, suffice it to say that one result is that the Earth is spinning. In antiquity, the Earth was considered motionless. After all, does it seem like we're spinning at 750 miles an hour at temperate latitudes and 1000 miles an hour at the equator? The Copernican revolution dispelled the idea of a motionless

Earth in the same way it removed Earth from the center of the universe.

The solar day is 24 hours, the time passage required for the Sun to return to the same position in the sky each day. Sidereal time is a time system based on the Earth's rotation relative to the stars rather than relative to the Sun. A sidereal day is 23 hours. 56 minutes, and 4.0905 seconds. The clocks on the walls in observatories display sidereal time. A star will return to view in the telescope every 23 hours, 56 minutes, and 4.0905 seconds. That time is the same time required to rotate exactly 360°. The Earth's orbit around the Sun causes the difference between a solar and a sidereal day.

The Earth rotates toward the east, which leaves the impression the Sun is rising in the east. It's more accurate to realize we are rotating toward the Sun and under it as we pass local noon.

The tidal effects of the Moon slow the Earth's rotation. Atomic clocks, and historical records of eclipses dating back 28 centuries, indicate that each century the Earth requires about two milliseconds longer to complete a turn.

The Three Gorges Dam in China, completed in 2012, dams the Yangtze River. The resulting lake holds a lot of water. The water that doesn't make it to the sea changed the distribution of mass on the Earth. A calculation by NASA figures this slowed the Earth's rotation by 0.06 microseconds each day. Don't forget to reset your clocks.

Coordinated Universal Time

Coordinated Universal Time (UTC) is the world's time standard, kept within one second of the mean solar time at 0° longitude. In 1884, Greenwich, England, was defined as 0° longitude. The time there soon became an international standard for time everywhere. UTC, sometimes referred to as Greenwich Mean Time (GMT), has the advantage that all clocks worldwide read the same time. For example, Neil Armstrong set foot on the Moon at different times at different places on Earth. It was Monday, July 21, 1969, at 2:56 UTC, or Sunday night in the United States at 10:56 pm EDT.

ZONE	SHIFT
EST	-5
EDT	-4
CST	-6
CDT	-5
MST	-7
MDT	-6
PST	-8
PDT	-7

Astronomers use UTC almost exclusively. The table shows how to shift UTC to local times in the United States. Because the Earth rotates eastward, the Sun rises in Europe before the United States. For example, noon UTC is 8:00 am EDT and 4:00 am PST.

The Year

The Earth requires 365.256 days to complete one revolution around the Sun, referred to as a sidereal year. The 0.25 results in a calendar correction called the leap year, which adds February 29 every four years. Skipping leap year every century, except those divisible by 400, corrects the 0.006 days. The last century we didn't skip a leap year was 2000. That won't happen again until 2400.

Around 1605, Kepler determined the Earth's orbit around the Sun is elliptical rather than circular. Remember from high school geometry how to draw an ellipse? You can draw a circle by looping a string around a tack on a drawing board and sweeping out a circle with a pencil at the other end of the loop. Put two tacks on the drawing board, and the swept figure is an ellipse. Either tack marks the location of the Sun, and the pencil draws the Earth's orbit. The assumption of an elliptical orbit rather than a circular orbit leads to a more accurate prediction of planetary positions amongst the stellar background. This is how Kepler figured out this ellipse thing in the first place. Our orbit is almost circular, but the Sun's distance varies by about 3% during the year.

The Seasons

Why is it cold in the Winter? Some answer because the Earth is farther from the Sun in the Winter. That makes perfect sense, but it isn't so. The Earth is closest to the Sun around January 3. It's about 3.1 million miles closer in January than when it's farthest around July 4. So why is it colder in Winter?

Most of you answer the question correctly because the Earth's axis tilts 23.4° with respect to its orbit around the Sun. As the Earth orbits the Sun, the Earth's rotational axis remains pointed to the right of vertical, as shown in the figure. The Northern Hemisphere is tilted away from the Sun during Winter. In the figure, imagine the Sun is to the left. The Sun is lower in the southern sky, and the glancing rays of the Sun are not so warming. Also, this tilt causes Winter days to be shorter, which also chills. Most of you knew all that, so let's get back to this distance from the Sun thing.

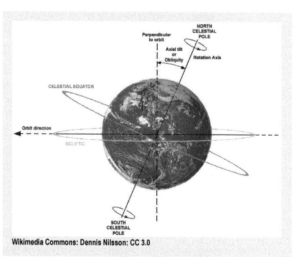

Wikimedia Commons: Dennis Nilsson: CC 3.0

On January 3rd, Earth is at perihelion. In Greek, "peri" means near and Helios is the Sun god. Earth is at aphelion, its farthest Sun distance, around July 4th. That it's colder when the Sun is closest indicates that the difference in distance is too small to impact the temperature significantly. Of course, Winter for us is the warm season in the Southern Hemisphere. And baby, now you know why it's cold outside in Winter.

Equinox and Solstice

On the day shown in the figure, the Earth's North Pole is at its maximum tilt away from the Sun. It's December, and it's the Winter solstice. The length of the day in the Northern Hemisphere is the shortest of the year. North of the arctic circle, the Sun never rises. The Sun is shining directly overhead on the Tropic of Capricorn, which circles the globe in the Southern Hemisphere at latitude -23.4°.

Now imagine it's March, and the Earth has rotated around the Sun counterclockwise, as seen from above. The Earth has moved into the paper of the figure and to the left. The Sun is now directly over the equator, and it's the Spring equinox. Day and night are of equal length everywhere on Earth. The Sun rises due east and sets due west.

As the Earth continues its annual orbit, the Sun is to the figure's right in June. It's the Summer solstice, and the Sun is directly overhead on the Tropic of Cancer which circles the globe at latitude 23.4°. It's the longest day in the Northern Hemisphere. The Sun never sets north of the arctic circle. Finally, the Sun is directly behind the Earth in the figure, and it's the Autumnal equinox. Again, day and night are of equal length, and the Sun rises due east and sets due west.

Even before calendars became formalized, ancient cultures used the equinoxes and solstices as date markers. Some structures and dwellings incorporated features related to these events. Today, the equinoxes and solstices remain notable events in culture.

Star Trails and Polaris

Consider this five-hour night-time photographic exposure. Because of the Earth's daily rotation during the exposure, the stars sweep out arcs. Polaris is the arc just to the left of the center of rotation. If Polaris were exactly north, it would have appeared as a point at the center of rotation. Stars to the right of Polaris are eastward. As the night progresses, they rise upward and over the top. Stars to the left are descending.

Wikimedia Commons: Anton Yankovyi: CC 4.0

This hour-long photographic exposure, taken Nepal's Himalayas, depicts the rotation of stars around the celestial north pole. Circumpolar stars near Polaris never set but just fade away with the coming of dawn. As you travel northward, the center of rotation rises higher in the sky. When you reach the North Pole, Polaris is directly overhead, and all the stars you see are circumpolar.

No natural law requires that Polaris should align with the rotational axis of the Earth. Polaris is about three-fourths of a degree off true north. That's accurate enough for a good Boy Scout to find his way back to camp at night, and I used it to plant my vineyard rows north-south. Polaris aligns with true north better than a compass because Earth's magnetic pole is in northern Canada and not at the geographic pole.

A common misconception is that Polaris is a bright star, but it isn't. It's about the 50th brightest star. Polaris is most easily found by following a line from the outer two stars of the bowl of the big dipper. The first star you come to with similar brightness to the bowl stars is Polaris. Like many stars, Polaris is not a single star, but three that are so close they appear as one. A small telescope splits Polaris into two visible stars, which William Hershel first observed in 1779. Polaris is often used to align small telescopes. When I do so, I know I have located Polaris because the pair is unmistakable once learned. The third star was discovered in 1929 by careful examination of the light spectrum of the triple system.

The next time you are out after dark for a while, watch the motion of stars around the North Star.

Precession

Polaris has not always been close to true north. The Earth's rotational axis is precessing. Envision a spinning toy top: when it's tilted relative to the floor, the top's axis sweeps out a circle in a motion called precession. The Earth's rotational axis is also precessing.

Three thousand years before Christ's birth, the Earth's rotational axis pointed toward the dim star Thuban in the constellation Draco, the serpentine dragon. The Earth's axis currently points within three-fourths of a degree of Polaris in Ursa Minor. In 14000 AD, the rotational axis will have swept around to point at the star Vega in the constellation Lyra. Vega is brighter than Polaris, and it's the star featured in the movie Contact. It takes roughly 26,000 years for our earthly top to sweep out one circle. It's a slow change, but the software that points my telescope must take precession into account.

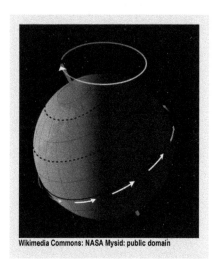

Wikimedia Commons: NASA Mysid: public domain

Ecliptic

Again, consider the figure on page 31. The celestial equator is an imaginary circle on the sphere of stars in the Heavens. It's perpendicular to the Earth's pole and in the same plane as the Earth's equator. Viewed from the Earth's equator, it passes through the zenith directly overhead. From the North Pole, it's the 360° circle of stars on the horizon in every direction. The beautiful constellations Orion and Leo are on the celestial equator.

Because of the Earth's tilt relative to our orbit around the Sun, the Sun appears on the celestial equator only during the equinoxes. In the Summer, the Sun appears well above the celestial equator, and in the Winter, it appears below the celestial equator. Because planets orbit in planes similar to the Sun, the planets wander through the Heavens near the ecliptic.

The ecliptic is the path through the Heavens that the Sun traces during the year. As the Earth rotates, we observe the stars sweeping through the Heavens in circles that are straight lines drawn on a rectangular map, much like latitude lines on a map. The Earth's rotational axis is tilted relative to the Sun, so the Sun appears to wander lower in the sky in the Winter and higher in the Summer. On a map, the ecliptic serpentines up and down across the celestial equator twice, as shown on page 98. The astrological Zodiac passes through thirteen constellations. Historically, astrologers conveniently divided the Zodiac into twelve equal 30° segments. However, these segments don't align with the constellations, which have unequal sizes. They also omitted the constellation of Ophiuchus.

Artificial Satellites

Earth's Moon is a satellite. Man-made satellites are referred to as artificial satellites, or often just satellites. Why don't the Moon and satellites fall back to Earth? Long before there were rockets to launch satellites, Newton figured out the theory. Consider Newton's cannon in the figure. When fired from a mountain, ball A falls to the foot of the mountain. When fired faster, as in case B, the ball falls farther from the mountain. If fired fast enough, as in case C, the ball travels away from the mountain as far as it falls. It's continually falling toward the Earth but traveling away from it as well. In case C, the ball is in free fall. If you are in a satellite orbiting the Earth, you and the cabin are falling together. You are weightless. The weight you feel on Earth is the Earth pushing back on your feet. No push back, no feeling of weight. In case D, the ball exceeds the minimum orbital velocity, and the satellite

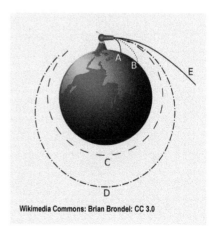

Wikimedia Commons: Brian Brondel: CC 3.0

orbit is elliptical. In case E, the ball exceeds the escape
velocity and never returns. Escape velocity is about 25,000
miles per hour for the Earth.

One of Newton's Laws of Motion is that an object in
motion stays in motion unless acted upon by force. On
Earth, drag and friction are forces that ultimately stop
things. When you roll a ball, friction eventually stops the
ball. It's intuitive to imagine that things want to stop, but
they don't. Think about trying to stop a rolling car even if
it's on flat ground. It takes a lot of force. In space, there is
little atmosphere, and a satellite keeps on moving.

So, to launch a satellite requires lifting the satellite
vertical to get it above the atmosphere and sideways fast
enough to put it in orbit. The required height is about 100
miles, and the needed speed at that altitude is about
17,000 miles per hour. The orbital period, the time it takes
to circle the Earth, is about 90 minutes. The launch of the
Sputnik I in October 1957 was a wake-up call that launched
the United States into the space race.

I remember an assigned problem in my college Physics
101 class. Imagine a hole through the center of the Earth to
the other side. Imagine there is no air to cause drag. Drop a
ball into the hole, and what happens? Given Newton's Law
of Gravity and Motion and a little math, it's not too difficult
to solve. The answer: the ball begins falling faster and
faster toward the center of the Earth. It's attracted to the
center of mass, which is the center of the Earth. It
continues to pick up speed until it reaches the center. As it
passes the center, the pull from the center begins to slow it
down. But inertia keeps it going as it rises upward to the
other side of the Earth. The force of gravity continues to
work on it, and the ball eventually stops at the surface. A
far-side citizen could reach out and grab it. If he doesn't, it
starts falling back and ultimately comes back to you. What
was the maximum speed at the center? It's 17,000 miles
per hour. How long does it take? Ninety minutes, the same
as the orbital period. It's a beautiful answer, which
cemented my love of physics and mathematics forever.

The Clark Belt

With increased orbital height, the force of Earth's gravity becomes smaller. Gravity's weaker force reduces the required velocity and increases the orbital period. At the height of 22,236 miles above mean sea level, the orbital period is 23 hours, 56 minutes, and 4 seconds, the sidereal day. The time it takes for one orbit is the same time for the Earth to rotate 360°. Therefore, a satellite remains over the same point on the equator. An antenna pointed at that satellite does not need to move to remain pointed at the satellite.

In 1945, the science-fiction writer Arthur C. Clark published an article predicting communication satellites in geostationary orbit. Others had written about stationary satellites, and Clark imagined them manned, but his prediction was prophetic nonetheless. The belt above the Earth's equator holding geostationary satellites is referred to as the Clark Belt.

Because it must be directly above the equator and at a specific height, the Clark Belt is valuable real estate. It holds your Dish and Direct-TV satellites and other communication and weather satellites. Because Antennas on the ground don't need to move, so they are simpler and less expensive to build. There are over 500 satellites in geostationary orbit. The International

Wikimedia Commons: James Vaughan: CC 2.0
ARTHUR C CLARK
(1917 - 2008) British science fiction writer and futurist on the set of his 2001, A Space Odyssey

Telecommunications Union (ITU) assigns operating frequencies for all radio spectrum users on Earth and in space, for that matter. It also assigns orbital slots in the Clark Belt. Above high-use areas, such as the United States and Europe, geostationary satellites are about 50 miles apart. The reason they are separated is not a danger of

collision. The reason is that ground station antenna
beamwidths are only so narrow. Closer satellite spacing
would cause signals transmitted to the satellites to
interfere with each other.

Observing Artificial Satellites

Observing artificial satellites is fun. Geostationary
satellites are too far away and therefore too dim to see
without a telescope. Larger satellites in low Earth orbit can
be bright. They move across the sky at about the speed
airplanes appear to move.

What you see on airplanes are their running lights. For
satellites, you see reflected sunlight. Observing satellites
requires the sky must be dark, but the Sun must still be
shining on the satellite. Closer satellites are brighter, so
satellites in low Earth orbit are brighter. However, low
orbit means that these satellites will be in the Earth's
shadow most of the night. Therefore, the best satellite
views are up to about 45 minutes after sunset or before
sunrise. The brightness also depends on the angle of
reflection off the satellite.

There are thousands of satellites in orbit around the
Earth. Away from town and during the dark of the Moon,
you can observe satellites by just relaxing in a lawn chair
and waiting for darkness. Most satellites are dim, but with
a little luck, you might see a bright one.

The brightest satellite is the International Space
Station (ISS). On
some passes, it
may appear
brighter than
Venus, the
brightest object in
the sky other than
the Moon or Sun.
But any given
satellite usually
makes only one,
sometimes two
passes per night.

Wikimedia Commons: NASA STS-132: public domain

For days at a time, the ISS may make visible passes only in daylight. You'll have a much better chance of seeing the ISS if you know when and where to look. NASA provides an online website that predicts when and where to look for the ISS. The NASA website is *spotthestation.nasa.gov*. My favorite satellite tracking website is *heavens-above.com*, which also lists less bright satellites. With either of these websites, you'll enter your city, or latitude and longitude, and the website provides information on when and where to look.

Twinkle, Twinkle, Little Star

Clean, dry air passes almost 100% of the light in the middle wavelengths of visible light, such as yellow. Air is clear, right? Light travels in a straight line. Sunlight from the Sun travels straight at us. Look away from the Sun, and the sky should be black as night. In space, the Sun and stars are visible at the same time. But at shorter wavelengths, like blue, the atmosphere scatters more light, making the sky look blue. When you look toward the horizon at the setting Sun, you are looking through a lot more atmosphere. The blue light from the Sun is scattered and weakened, and the Sun appears red. The light from haze and dust in the atmosphere is also reddened, thus causing beautiful sunsets.

But the air acts like a weak lens. That is what causes the Summer "mirage of a lake" on the road in front of you. If you look at the mirage closely, you'll see the shiny water appears to move and have waves. The air not only slightly bends the light, but it's also turbulent. This turbulence causes stars to twinkle, which is called scintillation. Even though you can't see the disk of planets with just your eyes, they do have a disk. However, starlight comes as a point of light. The disk of light from planets reduces the twinkle.

For astronomers, amateur and professional alike, the turbulence caused by the atmosphere is a disaster. As you magnify an object in the telescope with a higher power, the object's view becomes fuzzy and appears to be out of focus. That's the reason astronomers place observatories on mountains. No, folks, it not because the telescope is closer to the stars. With less atmosphere to travel through, there is less distortion in the image.

Telescopes provide two functions. The first is gathering more light from a large lens or mirror. Larger telescopes detect dimmer objects. The second function is magnifying the image, thus making the object look closer and providing more detail. Because of the turbulence, telescopes larger than about eight inches aperture fail to provide additional detail. Even amateur telescopes of that size are affordable. So, if they don't provide more detail, why are millions of dollars spent on large telescopes? Not for magnification, but for the light: to see dimmer objects.

The reason for the space telescope Hubble was to get above the atmosphere. Hubble is smaller than Earth-based telescopes, and space telescopes are expensive to launch, operate, and service. But the data collected with Hubble was free of atmospheric distortion. I'll talk about telescopes in a later chapter.

Meteors

As a small boy, my first memory of astronomy was falling asleep in a lawn chair while watching falling stars. Each is an anticipated but startling surprise, like the tug on your pole when a fish takes the bait. Some meteors are brilliant, others only perceptible. On a typical moonless night away from city lights, you'll see about one per hour.

Of course, falling stars are not stars at all, but bits of rock and iron. Most are the size of grains of sand to the size of walnuts, and air friction heats them as they enter the upper atmosphere at fantastic speeds. The larger ones produce dazzling displays that linger for a while. In space, these small bodies are called meteoroids. As they travel through the atmosphere, they are called meteors. If they make it to the ground, they are meteorites.

As the Earth orbits the Sun, it sometimes travels near areas where comets have traveled. Comets are like dirty snowballs. As a comet nears the Sun, it partially melts and leaves behind the debris. As the Earth passes through this debris, it's swept up and falls to the Earth as meteors. During these periods, the quantity of meteors increases, and it's called a shower. The word shower is a bit of an exaggeration. The sky doesn't fall, but the observable number of meteors may increase from one per hour up to one or two per minute. During a shower, meteors appear to emanate from a point in the sky called a radiant. The image here is a sketch of an observed shower. During a shower, these meteors would not be seen all at once but perhaps a minute apart. But over time, they appear to radiate from a point in space. The movement of the Earth and shower debris cause meteors to emanate from the direction of the radiant.

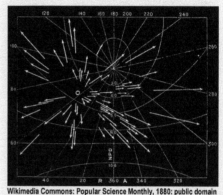

Wikimedia Commons: Popular Science Monthly, 1880: public domain

NAME	PEAK	ZHR	SPEED	COMET
Quadrantids	Jan 3	110	Med	Asteroid?
Lyrids	Apr 22	18	Med	C/1861 G1 (Thatcher)
Eta Aquarids	May 6	50	Fast	1P/Halley
Perseids	Aug 12	110	Fast	109P/Swift-Tuttle
Draconids	Oct 8	10	Slow	21P/Giacobini-Zinner
Orionids	Oct 21	20	Fast	1P/Halley
Leonids	Nov 17	15	Fast	55P/Tempel-Tuttle
Geminids	Dec 13	140	Slow	3200 Phaethon

Here is a table of some of the more prominent showers each year. PEAK is the day of the most significant shower intensity. The peak day varies somewhat each year, so it's a good idea to check the internet or your local news each year. For a few days around the peak, the quantity of meteors is higher than usual. ZHR is the zenith hourly rate looking straight up on a moonless night in dark skies. Some meteors appear to travel faster or slower than others. The speed column indicates whether a particular shower has slow or fast meteors. The final column is the comet believed to be associated with the shower.

To observe meteors, you won't need a telescope or a helmet either. The only person ever hit by a meteor was 32-year old Ann Hodges of Alabama in 1954. The nine-pound meteorite came through her roof, tore up the ceiling, bounced off her old radio, and hit her while she napped on a couch. She got a nasty bruise on her hip but was otherwise unhurt. The worst damage was to her mental, physical, and financial health, caused by a vicious legal battle over custody of the meteorite. Ultimately, she gave it to the Alabama Museum of Natural History in Tuscaloosa, where it's on display. This meteor was visible in daylight in three states.

Aurora

Auroras, beautiful displays of color and light, result from the solar wind interacting with the Earth's magnetosphere. Besides light and heat, the Sun radiates a vast wind of electrons, protons, alpha particles (helium nuclei), and traces of ionized atoms of heavier elements. The Sun emits over a million tons of this stuff each second. This wind travels outward from the Sun at velocities exceeding 600,000 miles per hour. When the solar wind crashes into the Earth's magnetic field, the Earth creates a

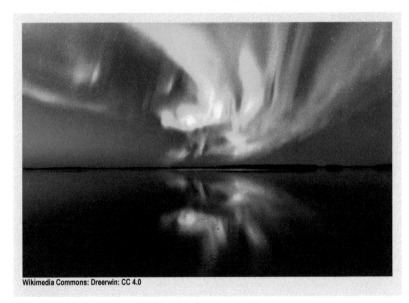

bow and tail wave like a boat in the water. The bow wave extends tens of thousands of miles in front of Earth, and the tail wave extends millions of miles behind the Earth.

These bow and tail waves interact with the Van Allen radiation belt detected by Explorer I in 1958 and credited to James Van Allen (1914 – 2006) for his radiation experiment onboard. Except for Earth's protective magnetic field, the Solar wind would be lethal. When that wind tangles with the magnetic field, the result is the beautiful aurora. It's typically seen only in the higher northern and southern latitudes. In the Northern Hemisphere, they are referred to as the Northern Lights or the Aurora Borealis. In the Southern Hemisphere, they are the Southern Lights or the Aurora Australis.

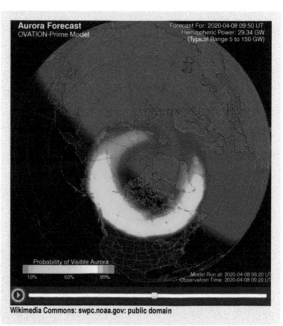

Wikimedia Commons: swpc.noaa.gov: public domain

Auroras are most prominent during periods of high solar activity. I remember beautiful Northern Lights in Illinois in the late 1950s when I was about 11 and in the late 1960s. By the next cycle in the late 1970s, I had moved to Atlanta, where they are rarely seen. I'll write about the solar cycle in the chapter, The Solar System.

During solar activity minimums, auroras are less frequent. The optimum zone to observe auroras is between 64° and 72° north latitude. That includes Alaska, northern Canada, Iceland, northern Scandinavia, and northern Russia. Of course, you also need darkness. In the far north, that means from Fall to Spring. The National Oceanic and Atmospheric Administration (NOAA) provides a short-term aurora forecast service with a typical computer screen shown here.

Light Pollution

To turn night into day, modern man generates a lot of light. All that light goes somewhere, and a lot of it's up. Creating that light also generates a lot of heat and uses fossil fuel. It's a mess. It's a disaster for both professional and amateur astronomers. It's also a disaster for anyone who wants to look up and enjoy the Heavens. One-third of humanity and 80% of Americans can't see the Milky Way from where they live.

All industrial cities generate massive light pollution. In the United States, the northeastern coastal area, Atlanta, Florida, and the California coast are significant polluters. Even my hometown, with only about 19,000 residents, is easily located on this nighttime photograph from space. Notice that the only truly dark areas of the United States

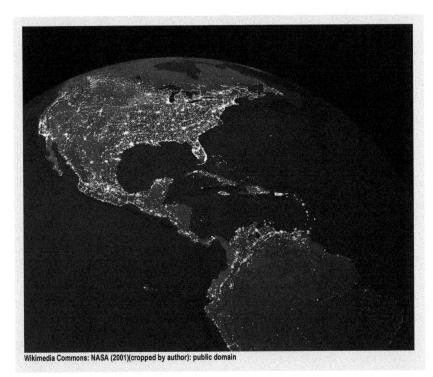

Wikimedia Commons: NASA (2001)(cropped by author): public domain

are isolated areas east of the Cascade mountains and west of the Mississippi River. The generation of light consumes 20 to 25% of the energy generated in the United States.

Of course, lighting is essential for specific tasks and safety. But sadly, much lighting is inefficient and goes where it isn't needed. Glare, which is light that shines directly into your eyes, and light that shines upward, is wasted. Airplanes don't need the light. Billboards and building lighting are significant offenders. The International Dark-Sky Association is a non-profit that works "*to preserve and protect the nighttime environment and our heritage of dark skies through quality outdoor lighting.*" Newer light fixtures direct less light upward. However, increasing urbanization and lights directed upward for buildings and signs continue to proliferate. Areas with economic impact from professional astronomy have enacted aggressive lighting ordnances. Several states provide guidelines for local ordinances.

Mankind is not the only light polluter. On many nights, the bright glow of the Moon washes away the Milky Way and the dimmer stars. But that gives us a chance to enjoy another beautiful Heavenly body, the Moon, covered in chapter four. But first, let's consider the telescope.

3 Telescopes

All you need to enjoy many beautiful objects in the Heavens are your eyes. However, as Galileo discovered, optical aid provides a new vision. As you probe further from Earth, sometimes your eyes will suffice, but other times optical aid will help. If you own a pair of binoculars, you can probe deeper than Galileo. I'll provide some tips in case you want to invest in a telescope. I'll also cover the history of the instruments that scientists use to explore the Heavens.

Optics

You already possess an optical instrument, actually two, your eyes. The cornea and a smaller lens behind it focus light on your retina, the light-sensitive portion of your eyes. The distance from the cornea to the retina determines the image's size, as interpreted by your brain. Actually, your brain is pretty busy. The images on the retina are upside down. Your brain fixes that. The eyes provide two signals to the brain. Because of parallax and the roughly 2.5-inch separation of your eyes, the two images have closer objects in different places. Your brain not only provides depth perception from the two images but also puts them back together to form one image.

Light travels at the speed of light only in a vacuum. In other media, such as water, your cornea, or glass, light is slower. This causes two effects. Some of the light is reflected. The light that passes through is bent in a process referred to as refraction. Glass lenses that shape the refracted light are designed using classic geometry laws. Telescopes designed this way are called refracting telescopes or refractors. Telescopes designed using mirrors are referred to as reflecting telescopes or reflectors.

Astronomical optical instruments are helpful for two reasons. Look at your eyes in the bathroom mirror. In dim light, the diameter of your pupil is about a quarter inch. Acuity or resolution, the ability to see detail, improves with the diameter of a lens or mirror. A telescope with a three-inch lens resolves distant objects with twelve times the detail of unaided eyes. Resolution is different than magnification which I'll describe later. Consider that resolution is detail. The larger the diameter of the telescope lens, the more detail it can resolve in distant objects. But there is another advantage of the telescope.

Distant astronomical objects like nebulae and galaxies are dim, very dim. Light gathering power improves with the lens area rather than the diameter, and the area increases with the square of the diameter. So, our three-inch lens gathers 144 times as much light as the eye.

Binoculars

Binoculars are two telescopes mounted side-by-side. Modern binoculars use sophisticated optical technology but are simple to use. Their performance exceeds that of Galileo's primitive telescopes. My advice to those just getting into astronomy is to buy a pair of binoculars rather than a telescope. Binoculars are easier to use, are good practice for using a telescope, and help you make a wiser telescope purchase later. The binoculars can be used for other tasks, and many heavenly objects are better viewed with binoculars than with telescopes.

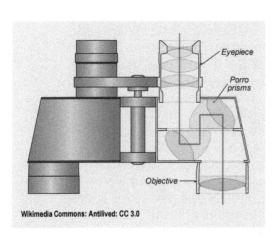

Binoculars are primarily marketed using two parameters: the magnification and the objective lens diameter. For example, a pair of 7X35 binoculars have a magnification of 7 and a front lens diameter of 35 millimeters(mm). There are 25.4 millimeters in an inch, so this lens diameter is about 1.4 inches. The Moon and planets are bright, but deep space objects like nebulae and galaxies are dim. Because larger objectives gather more light, 50mm or 70mm objectives are preferred. The diameter of the objective lens is referred to as the aperture. A larger aperture provides better views but is heavier, and above 70mm, you'll need a tripod. If you already have a pair of 7x35 binoculars, don't be discouraged, give them a try. They'll reveal far more than your eyes alone.

The objective and eyepiece lens of telescopes and binoculars typically invert the image. Binoculars use prisms to erect the image. The two most common forms of binoculars are Porro prism binoculars shown in the image and roof prisms which keep the eyepiece in line with the objective. Porro prisms transmit more light and are preferred for astronomy.

Exit pupil is another important parameter for binoculars used for astronomy. Light exits the eyepiece within a diameter equal to the objective diameter divided by the magnification. Pupil diameter in the dark is about 7mm in a young person and typically becomes less with age, down to about 5mm. The light outside this diameter does not enter the eye and is wasted. Therefore, popular ratings of 6x35, 7x50, 10x50, and 10x70 work best for astronomy. Holding steady heavy binoculars with larger objectives is a problem. Binoculars on tripods are a problem because the tripod is where you need to stand when looking up.

Another important parameter is eye relief, which is how far behind the eyepiece your eyes need to be for the best view. Closer than 9mm may be uncomfortable. If you are nearsighted, glasses significantly improve your enjoyment of the Heavens. Taking glasses on and off while using binoculars is a nuisance. To use binoculars with your glasses on requires eye relief of 15 mm or more.

Finally, the field of view (FOV) is another binocular parameter. It's specified as either the width of the view in feet at 1000 yards or in degrees. For birding and sporting events, keeping up with the action is easier with a wider

FOV. This is less important in astronomy, and state-of-the-art FOV performance adds cost.

One of the issues most users have with binoculars is holding the image steady. Observing detail in a small but bright planet or a large but dim nebula requires a steady image. This is a challenge with binoculars. Canon makes high-quality, image-stabilized binoculars. When you zero in on a target and hold the binoculars almost steady, electronics stabilize the image. The catch: they're expensive and require batteries.

In the remainder of the book, I'll point out Heavenly objects to enjoy with binoculars. There are some excellent books devoted to more advanced binocular astronomy, including *Touring the Universe through Binoculars* by Philip Harrington and *Binocular Astronomy* by Craig Crossen and Wil Tirion.

Refracting Telescopes

Galileo's telescope used a single convex lens objective as shown at the top of the diagram and a single concave eyepiece lens. It produced an erect image but had low magnification, a narrow FOV, and multiple distortions.

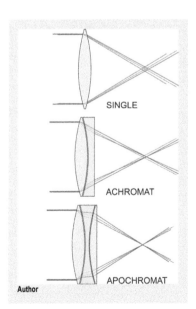

Nevertheless, Galileo discovered the phases of Venus, craters, and mountains on the Moon, and four moons circling Jupiter.

The speed of light is slower in glass than in air, and the light that enters the curved glass lens is bent. Shorter wavelengths (blue) are bent more than red light. This is how a prism disperses white light into a colorful spectrum. But a star should look like a sharp point, not a smear of color. The lens's focal length is the distance from the lens to the focus, where the light from the lens converges. The single lens brings the blue, green, and red light into focus at different focal lengths. The result is an image with chromatic distortion, or "false color."

Other aberrations also occur. Light from the lens's edge does not converge to the same focus as light closer to the middle of the lens, and light entering at an angle is not correctly focused. Increasing the lens's focal length reduces these distortions. Early astronomers discovered that doubling the lens aperture required increasing the focal length four times to reduce the false color. This resulted in the construction of very long telescopes. By the late 17th century, the length became so extreme that the aerial telescope was developed. The heaviest portion of the telescope, the tube, was eliminated. The observer pulled a cord to point the objective and held the eyepiece in a short tube on a stand.

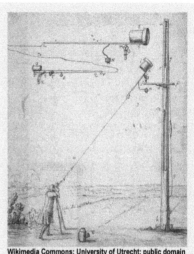

Wikimedia Commons: University of Utrecht: public domain

Newton believed the false-color problem was fundamental and could not be overcome. However, by the mid-1700s, opticians developed the achromat, which used two glass types with different refraction indices. This allows two different colors to achieve focus and reduces the other distortions. But still, to achieve good image quality, the focal length must be long. The result is the classic-looking long telescope of relatively small diameter.

An apochromat objective uses a triplet lens to focus three wavelengths of light. Apochromats provide even less false color than achromats. However, they utilize a modern glass that is expensive. Advanced amateur astronomers use apochromatic telescopes to take high-quality digital photographs of the Heavens.

The most critical parameter for an astronomical telescope is the aperture of the objective. This gathers more

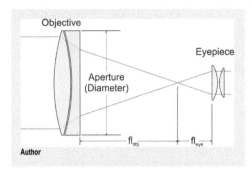

Author

light and improves resolution. The aperture is typically specified in millimeters. The aperture of amateur telescope objectives is usually 80 mm to 150 mm, with the larger sizes being rather expensive. Another critical parameter is the speed of the objective. As with cameras, this is typically given as the f ratio. It's the focal length of the objective divided by its aperture. For example, a telescope with an 80mm diameter objective with a focal length of 720 mm is $f9$. The third parameter for a telescope is magnification. This is the objective focal length divided by the eyepiece focal length. Unlike binoculars, telescopes typically come with multiple eyepieces to provide different magnifications. For example, using an eyepiece with a focal length of 24 mm results in a magnification of 30 with the example objective. I'll use these parameters later when discussing purchasing and using a telescope.

Reflecting Telescopes

Reflecting telescopes operate similarly to refracting telescopes, except they use a primary mirror to gather and focus the light. Reflectors also use an additional mirror and an eyepiece. Diameter, f ratio, and magnification are defined similarly to the refractor. Large lenses are more expensive to manufacture than large mirrors, so amateur

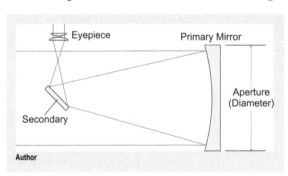

Author

reflectors with mirrors larger than 150mm are common. Because mirrors do not have false color, the f ratio of reflectors is typically faster than refractors. The primary mirror rear support and the secondary mirror holder require occasional user adjustment. The secondary mirror is not a lens but is flat.

Isaac Newton invented this type of telescope because he knew a mirror would avoid the false color of a lens. Others had conceived of using a mirror to replace the objective lens, but Newton probably built the first reflector. Newton used metal for the mirror. Telescopes today use glass with a reflective coating. One challenge is grinding the glass for the mirror to be a true parabola with an error less than a fraction of a wavelength of light.

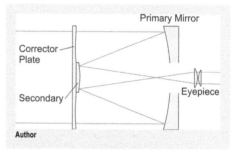

Changing the secondary flat to a shaped mirror and placing a hole in the primary mirror results in the Cassegrain telescope family. Laurent Cassegrain (c. 1629-1693) first diagrammed the idea. Placing the eyepiece behind the primary folds the light path, reduces the telescope tube length by two, and creates a compact design that saves weight. Shown here is a Schmidt-Cassegrain. The corrector plate is named for Bernhard Schmidt (1879-1935), a German optician. The corrector plate is a weak lens that corrects some distortions and allows both the primary and secondary mirrors to be spherical, thus reducing manufacturing costs. This design is popular with amateur astronomers. A more expensive Cassegrain type design that doesn't require a corrector is a Ritchey-Chrétien telescope (RCT). This is the University of Denver's former 24inch RCT, which the author purchased and moved to New Mexico and used from 1996 to 2008.

How to Buy a Telescope

As mentioned previously, the best way to start exploring the Heavens with optical aid is using binoculars. Binoculars are more powerful than the telescope that Galileo turned on the Heavens and turned astronomy upside down. After using binoculars for a while, you'll discover your interests, and selecting the right telescope becomes easier.

Most of us live under skies with some light pollution. The Moon, planets, double stars, and some of the brighter nebulae and galaxies are enjoyable even in those conditions. For best viewing, other objects require darker skies. While a larger objective or mirror is better, portability is a plus for an evening trip to darker skies. Some larger scopes are still affordable, but the size makes transport more difficult.

I suggest a modest investment for your first telescope. An 80 mm or 90 mm refractor gathers two or three times more light than a pair of 50 mm binoculars. The mount, included with the telescope, allows higher magnification which would be unsteady in binoculars. Entry-level refractors use an achromatic doublet object. The false color will be a problem with any achromat faster than $f6$. A better choice would be $f8$ to $f10$. You may have to dig into the specifications to find the telescope speed. Equatorial mounts, described in the next section, are preferred. If the seller boasts about magnification, then move on to another seller. Magnification is discussed in the section on how to use a telescope. Like binoculars, refractors require little maintenance. A telescope of this type costs from $150 to $400. A step up in the 80mm class is apochromats with faster speeds, shorter tubes, and no false color, but they cost about $800.

If your interest is deep-sky objects like nebulae and galaxies rather than the Moon or planets, you'll want a telescope that gathers more light. A good choice would be a reflector with a 130 mm to 180 mm mirror. They are slightly less portable but still manageable. The mounting systems for the primary and secondary mirrors of reflectors are sensitive to jarring and transport. These systems occasionally need adjustment, called collimation, and instructions found at many websites. A telescope of this type costs from \$350 to \$500.

For years, the workhouse of amateur astronomy has been the Schmidt-Cassegrain. A 200mm Schmidt-Cassegrain offers plenty of light-gathering power, a shorter tube, and excellent resolution. It's a worthy investment as you step up your observing. A telescope of this type costs \$1000 to \$2000.

You may need support or service. I suggest a reputable brick-and-mortar reseller. The chapter Resources lists resellers that specialize in optics.

Telescope Mounts

The mount is a critical element of a practical telescope. It must not only support the telescope, but it aids in finding objects and keeping them in view as the Earth turns. Using a telescope, magnification of 100 or more is common. This magnifies a hundred times any vibrations in the mount and the objects' movement as the Earth turns.

There are many variations on the two basic mount types. The first type is azimuth-elevation (Az-El) mounts where one axis is vertical to the ground and rotates the telescope in azimuth. The other axis is horizontal to the ground and controls the elevation of the telescope. Az-El mounts are standard for artillery. They are simple, sturdy, and inexpensive. However, as the Earth rotates, both the azimuth and elevation must be adjusted.

Wikimedia Commons: Marie-Lan Nguyen: CC 2.5

Shown here is a Cassegrain telescope mounted on the second type, an equatorial mount. The mount axis pointed upward located above the orange circle is the equatorial axis. You adjust the mount so this axis points toward the Earth's celestial pole near the North Star, Polaris. The other axis holding the counterweights is the declination axis. It points the telescope north and south of the celestial equator. Only the equatorial axis must turn to compensate for the Earth's rotation, and this axis may have either manual slow-motion control or a motor to track celestial objects with time. When motorized, it's referred to as a clock drive. The Az-El mount is handiest for birding and terrestrial viewing, while the equatorial mount is superior for astronomy. An Az-El mount is simpler to manufacture, and with the advent of computer control chips, an Az-El mount is sometimes equipped with a motor for each axis and computer programming to keep the scope tracking.

Another modern enhancement is a go-to mount. One of the challenges facing novice amateur astronomers is pointing the telescope at the desired object. Even if you can easily see the target, such as a bright planet, at higher magnification, the field of view in the telescope is fractions of a degree. Once a go-to telescope is set up, the user simply selects the desired object from a list. While this sounds convenient, the telescope still requires initial alignment. Go-to scopes aid in finding many objects in a night, but they need practice to operate.

Celestial Coordinates

Astronomers specify the locations of objects in the Heavens using equatorial coordinates. The system is analogous to Earth coordinates using latitude and longitude. One plane is the celestial equator, and the angle above or below the celestial equator is called declination, or DEC, and it's analogous to latitude. DEC is expressed in decimal degrees, or degrees, minutes, and seconds. For example, the upper right star in Orion's belt, Mintaka, is just south of the celestial equator at 0.299°S, or -00° 17' 57". The maximum declinations are 90°S and 90°N.

The second plane is perpendicular to the celestial equator and passes through the vernal equinox in the constellation Pisces, where the ecliptic intersects the celestial equator. This is called right ascension, or RA, and it's analogous to longitude. Right ascension is measured in hours, minutes, and seconds. It increases to the east up to 24h. Mintaka is at 5h 33m 01s RA. If Pisces is due south at midnight, Mintaka will be due south at 5:33 am.

Equatorially mounted telescopes may have two setting circles, one attached to the declination axis and one attached to the equatorial axis. These circles let you quickly point the telescope at objects with known DEC and RA.

How to Use a Telescope

So, your new telescope arrived. It's now unpacked and assembled. When I was a boy, I spent my savings on a 76mm reflector for $29.95 from Edmund Scientific. It arrived mid-Winter, and the weather was cloudy for two weeks. Hopefully, you'll be luckier.

Your scope may be a telescope for astronomy, but practicing during the day on distant, non-moving objects is a good idea. Your telescope probably came with more than one eyepiece. Eyepieces are marked with their focal lengths, such as 25mm, or f=25mm. For your first observation, chose the eyepiece with the longest focal length. This is the lowest magnification and makes objects easier to find. Choose the furthest object you can see, such as the top of a distant tree. Focus the telescope, and leave the focus in that position in preparation for nighttime observing.

Eyepieces are interchangeable in telescopes. If you step up to a larger telescope later, you can use your old eyepieces, and you can buy better eyepieces for your first telescope. Over time, you may go through a few telescopes but keep your eyepieces. Additional eyepieces are a good investment.

At night, the Moon or one of the planets make a good first target. The section Refracting Telescopes described how to calculate the magnification, but the same principle applies to reflectors.

Your telescope probably came with a finder. The finder may be a miniature telescope, a tube, or a reflex sight. While pointing the telescope in the direction of your target, look through the finder and center the target in the finder. The finder may need to be adjusted, so this is hit and miss at first. Finders on moderately priced telescopes are often of poor quality. I sometimes just get behind the telescope and align the target along the edge of the telescope. You need to do this with both azimuth and elevation. Next, look through the eyepiece, and if the object is not visible, slowly move the scope as you continue looking through the eyepiece. The target may be just a blur of light because the telescope is not focused. As you keep the blur centered, adjust the eyepiece focus for the smallest and brightest light. The blur comes to focus. There they are! - the rings of Saturn, or the moons of Jupiter, or Venus with a crescent, or craters on the Moon. Imagine the stunned surprise of Galileo 400 years ago.

The Great Telescopes

Aerial refractors held the lens size record for telescopes for 50 years, culminating in the 8.5-inch objective of Christiaan Huygens (1629 – 1695) in 1686. In 1734, a 14" Scottish reflector took the record for the largest optical telescope. Reflectors have held the record ever since. An American solar astronomer, George Ellery Hale (1868 –

1938), approached a Chicago businessman, Charles Yerkes, to build an observatory at the University of Chicago where Hale was a professor. The Yerkes Observatory pictured here held a 40-inch refractor completed in 1897. To limit false color, the telescope had a speed of *f*19, so it had a very long tube.

Wikimedia Commons: Jtakemann: public domain

The entire back of a reflector's mirror can be supported, but a refractor's lens must be supported at the edge only. To avoid sag, the glass must be so thick it isn't practical with larger apertures. As telescopes grew in size, reflectors took the size lead, which they never relinquished. The Yerkes Refractor remains to this day the largest refractor ever used for astronomical research. Having outlived its useful life, Yerkes Observatory was closed to the public in 2018.

George Hale was a tireless promoter of professional astronomy in both the United States and internationally. He discovered sunspots' magnetic nature and determined that the well-known 11-year sunspot cycle is actually a 22-year cycle with a polarity switch. As

Wikimedia Commons: photographer unknown: public domain

GEORGE ELLERY HALE
(1868 - 1938) American solar astronomer and developer of great telescopes

a gift from his father, Hale received a 60-inch mirror blank cast in France, and he secured funds from the Carnegie Institute to complete the 60-inch Hale telescope on Mt Wilson in California. Upon completing the 60-inch Hale, Hale immediately began plans for the 100-inch Hooker telescope on Mt. Wilson by securing initial funds from John Hooker, an ironmaster and philanthropist, and follow-up funding by Carnegie. It was using the 100-inch Hooker telescope that Edwin Hubble made a discovery that would profoundly change astronomy.

But Hale's planning and promotional masterpieces were the 200-inch Great Hale Telescope on Mt. Palomar in California. The Rockefeller Foundation provided funding of $88 million in today's dollars, and it took 20-years to plan and complete in 1949. Unfortunately, Hale never saw it finished. It remained the largest telescope in the world for 30 years. When I was young, my father took me to see the Great Hale Telescope. I had read a book about its construction, and I was in awe. Later, the 238-inch Russian

Author

BTA-6 took the size record, but it's plagued with multiple issues and has never reached its potential. The size record for a fully operational telescope was taken 44 years later in 1993 by the 396-inch Keck Observatory on Mt. Mauna Kea, Hawaii.

Today, the largest telescope is the Great Canary Telescope in the Canary Islands, completed in 2007 at the cost of roughly $178 million. Currently being planned for 2022 is the European Extremely Large Telescope in Chile, with a mirror diameter of 1560 inches and an estimated cost of $1.34 billion.

The need is for light, light that is gathered and focused on various instruments. Recall what Pope penned: *Nature and nature's laws lay hid in night; God said "Let Newton be" and all was light.*

Radio Telescopes

Up to the 1940s, astronomy flourished by observing only light, but that was about to change. In the early 1930s, Karl Jansky (1905 – 1950) worked at Bell Telephone Laboratories in Murry Hill, New Jersey, on a transatlantic radio system. His system recorded static he couldn't initially explain. The static peaked near the same time each day, and Jansky initially thought it was coming from the Sun. But then he noticed it peaked every 23 hours 56 minutes rather than every 24 hours. An astrophysicist friend pointed out that was a sidereal day, the period stars and other deep space objects take to return to the same position. He soon isolated it to the constellation Sagittarius in the direction of the center of the Milky Way. It was the first known observation of a celestial object by radio waves.

Hearing about Jansky's discovery, Grote Reber, an electrical engineer and amateur radio operator, constructed a radio telescope in his backyard in Wheaton, Illinois. He had just graduated from what is now the Illinois Institute of Technology and wanted to make radio astronomy his life work. He applied at Bell Labs, but no positions were available. He worked at radio manufacturers while pursuing his passion for radio astronomy. For a decade, he was the world's only radio astronomer, amateur or otherwise.

Wikimedia Commons: NRAO: public domain

GROTE REBER
(1911 - 2002) First radio astronomer

During this time, he published a radio map of the Heavens and ultimately became a professional astronomer. His backyard radio telescope was groundbreaking, and he later sold it to the National Bureau of Standards. Reber's ashes are located at radio observatories throughout the world.

Because radio waves are longer than light waves, radio telescopes must be enormous to provide good resolution. The world's largest fully steerable radio telescope dish is the Green Bank Telescope in West Virginia. Nevertheless, the antenna beamwidth is so wide that it's difficult to associate the signal with an optical object.

The next important step in radio telescopes was linking separate telescopes together to create a large virtual size or aperture, as it's called. Linked telescopes are called interferometers. At first, interferometers used several dishes at one site. With advancing technology, it became possible to link radio telescopes around the world.

Radio astronomy is now an essential tool. Sagittarius A, a radio source at the center of our galaxy, the Milky Way,

Wikimedia Commons: NRAO: public domain

was an early discovery of radio telescopes. It turns out Sagittarius A is a supermassive black hole.

Space Telescopes

As seen in this figure, the atmosphere is transparent to visible light and specific radio wavelengths. However, the atmosphere is opaque at infrared, ultraviolet, and X-ray wavelengths. Today, space-borne telescopes eliminate this barrier. The study of the Heavens in all of the various wavelengths of Maxwell's electromagnetic spectrum provides synergy in the ongoing search for knowledge about the universe.

NASA began investigating the possibility of a space-based telescope around 1970, and Congress began funding the project in 1978. After numerous project delays and cost overruns, the Hubble Space Telescope was launched onboard the Shuttle Discovery on April 24, 1990. NASA named Hubble for the astronomer Edwin Hubble who I'll bring up again in the chapter Deep Space.

Surprisingly, Hubble is a relatively small telescope. The performance of a telescope is related to the size of the primary mirror. The Hubble mirror is 94.5 inches in diameter. By comparison, sixty telescopes around the world are larger, some much larger. Launching, maintaining, and operating a telescope in orbit is far more

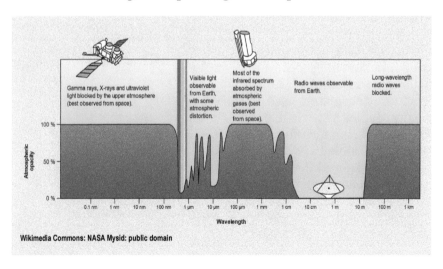

Wikimedia Commons: NASA Mysid: public domain

expensive than an Earth-based telescope. Hubble has cost every man, woman, and child in the US about $30. What justifies the considerable expense of a relatively small telescope in space?

The atmosphere bends light ever so slightly, and the atmosphere is turbulent. As a result, the atmosphere blurs the image of astronomical objects. It's similar to the distortion of a fish you view through the ripples of a clear stream. Because Hubble orbits above the atmosphere, images are much sharper than Earth-based telescopes. The larger Earth-based scopes gather more light, which

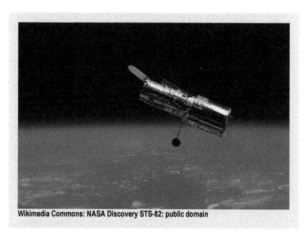

Wikimedia Commons: NASA Discovery STS-82: public domain

is also essential, but Hubble sees more detail.

As initially built, Hubble's mirror was flawed. Consequently, the first images were heartbreaking. Because NASA kept accurate records, they soon discovered the manufacturing error. Corrective optics, much like eyeglasses, were built and installed during a Shuttle service mission. The repair worked, and Hubble's boon to science has been stunning. Hubble reaches deep into space, and since light takes time to travel, deep in space is deep in time. Using Hubble, researchers accurately measured the universe's expansion rate, research that resulted in Noble Prizes. Closer to home, planetary science has been advanced. Over 9000 scientific papers have resulted from Hubble data.

Beautiful photo-shopped images are published regularly. There is no close-up vantage point in space where you would see these images. They have been photo-shopped and are as much art as science. But these beautiful images enamor the public and boost support for NASA.

With the shuttle fleet retired, NASA can no longer service Hubble, and it's near the end of its useful life. A sophisticated and relatively new technology called adaptive optics can unscramble some of the turbulence caused by the atmosphere. Adaptive optics and the colossal mirror size achievable with Earth-based telescopes almost eliminated the need for space-based optical telescopes. Nevertheless, Hubble was a revolutionary tool unlocking the mysteries hidden in the light and revealing the Heavens' beauty.

But Hubble is not the end of the space telescope story. Red is the lowest frequency of visible light. Lower still is the electromagnetic radiation called infrared. We feel a portion of the infrared spectrum as heat. The atmosphere is opaque to much of the infrared spectrum. At those frequencies, Earth-based telescopes can't see through the atmosphere. Also, the heat in the atmosphere and on Earth overwhelms infrared telescopes. The study of the infrared Heavens is best done from space.

The next phase of space-based astronomy is the planned James Webb Space Telescope (JWST). NASA began planning the JWST in 1996 and initially scheduled the launch for 2007. The JWST has suffered from numerous schedule slips and cost overruns. JWST is now

scheduled for an October 2021 launch. Advanced design technologies provide a mirror larger even than the Great Hale Telescope, 260 inches, with a spacecraft weight less than the 94-inch Hubble. Just as important, it's sensitive deep into the infrared. A successful mission would be a significant advance in astronomy.

Wikimedia Commons: NASA: Public domain

The mission involves risk, perhaps as great as the reward. The JWST will be kept at -370°F to reduce noise from its own heat. To remain cold, the JWST includes a shield to block the Sun from the telescope. But at that temperature, the Earth's heat is a problem as well. The shield must simultaneously block heat from both the Sun and the Earth, so the spacecraft is positioned 930,000 miles from Earth, almost four times the Moon's distance. The JWST is not serviceable; it has to work. NASA serviced Hubble five times. Only time will tell if the JWST produces tears or joy.

Hubble is not the only space telescope. NASA operated four space telescopes which they called the four Great Observatories. The most famous of the four, Hubble, explored the visible spectrum. In 2020, Hubble was near the end of its long life but still provided useful science. The Spitzer Space Telescope was launched in 2003 and explored the infrared spectrum, but NASA decommissioned it. The JWST will replace both of these space telescopes. The third Great Observatory, launched in 1991 aboard Atlantis, is the Compton Gamma Ray Observatory. Its mission was to study gamma rays, a very high frequency, and short-wavelength electromagnetic radiation. The Compton conducted science for eight years, but after a gyro failed, NASA intentionally deorbited the telescope into the Pacific. The fourth Great Observatory is the Chandra X-ray Observatory launched aboard the shuttle Columbia in 1999. X-rays are electromagnetic radiation at short wavelengths between the ultraviolet and gamma rays. As of this writing, Chandra remains operational.

Many countries operate other smaller space-based telescopes that draw less attention but yet provide important science. They share a common goal; exploring a portion of the electromagnetic spectrum inaccessible to Earth-based telescopes.

Gravity Waves

We thus come to the latest wave used in the quest for knowledge; gravity waves. Gravity is the warping of space itself by massive objects. This bending of space causes objects to seek a lower level, much like a ball would roll into a valley of a curved surface. The Earth pulls on us because it's bending the space beneath our feet. When two very massive objects, such as distant black holes, merge during the last phase of a violent death spiral, they cause a gravity ripple in space. Like light and radio waves, the ripples propagate at the speed of light. In 1916, Einstein predicted gravity waves' existence but felt scientists could never confirm his theory. The instrument sensitivity required to detect even the most catastrophic events the universe can muster is mind-boggling. It has taken a century of technology and equipment advances to detect gravity waves. These catastrophic events change the diameter of the Earth by the diameter of an atom. But the quest for knowledge is insatiable, and science was up to the task. On September 14, 2015, the first detection of gravity waves occurred at the Laser Interferometer Gravitational-Wave Observatory (LIGO) in Washington state. Since then, additional events have been detected. Don't worry - gravity waves won't rattle your dishes.

Low-Hanging Fruit

The cost of modern telescopes is truly astronomical. The European Extremely Large Telescope will cost over a billion US dollars just to build, and that doesn't include the operational cost. The cost of the James Webb Space Telescope is approaching ten billion dollars. Galileo changed the world-view by making discoveries with a handheld telescope he constructed. A pair of modern binoculars would outperform his telescope. Newton, who defined the scientific revolution, used a glass prism and a pen. In the 1930s, the United States annually graduated a few hundred Ph.Ds. From the 1970s to today, the number of PhDs conferred annually has climbed from 30,000 to over 50,000. Annual national funding for science rose from millions in the 1950s to over 40 billion dollars. According to a November 2018 article by Patrick Collision and Michael Nielson in The Atlantic magazine, a survey of 93 renowned international physicists indicated the Nobel Prizes awarded in the 1910s through the 1930s were as important, if not more so, than in recent decades.

The study of the evolution of stars and the Big Bang intertwines with nuclear physics. The University of California Berkley conducted particle research in 1932 with an 11-inch diameter particle accelerator. The Large Hadron Collider used to discover the Higgs boson particle is in a tunnel that is 17 miles in diameter underneath the France-Switzerland border. It cost over four billion dollars. Ernest Rutherford discovered the atom has a positively charged nucleus using a simple lab, and he singlehandedly wrote a Nobel Prize-winning paper. The two 2012 papers describing the discovery of the Higgs boson had over a thousand authors, each.

What is happening? It's a matter of low-hanging fruit. When science was young, the fruit was easy to pick. But the nature of science is such that as the fruit is picked, the remaining fruit is harder to reach. Perhaps, even, the tree grows taller. The optimist says, yes, but each scientist stands on the shoulders of the last. The pessimist says, what difference does it make that we know the universe is 13.799 billion years old or 20 billion? The optimist reminds us when Heinrich Hertz first demonstrated radio waves at the Royal Academy, and attendees asked what use they were, he responded *"nothing, I guess."* The pessimist says the heyday of science is over. Every answer has always raised two new questions, but scientists still seek the "ultimate" theory. Each advance will be more costly until progress becomes untenable.

The ever-receding "end answer" is another subject Einstein weighed in on, albeit long before the issue reached the current state of affairs, so his comments were prescient. A 1919 essay of his was titled *Induction and Deduction in Physics*. Induction is the process of considering the results of an experiment and developing an explanatory theory. Deduction is the process of developing a theory by extending accepted principles. Induction is the basis of experimental science, and as it advances, progress requires ever more elusive experimental data. Deduction is somewhat like mathematics and is how Einstein developed his theories of relativity. Einstein had a knack for understanding which "accepted principles" to accept and which to discard. In his essay, he wrote, *"...the big advances in scientific knowledge originated in this way [induction] only to a small degree,"* and then he wrote, *"The longer and the more despairingly I tried, the more I came to the conviction that only the discovery of a universal formal principle could lead us to assured results [deduction]."*

You may take your own position in the debate of how much and where to invest in science. Next, as we explore the Heavens, we will leave the Earth behind and head to where man has boldly gone before: the Moon.

4 The Moon

The Moon is a natural satellite of the Earth. Its motion follows the same laws as artificial satellites. Other bodies in our Solar System, including planets, dwarf planets, and even asteroids, also have moons, hundreds of them. The Moon is by far the largest in the Solar System relative to the host planet's size.

The Moon

The word Moon derives from the Old English mona, which means month. Luna is sometimes used to signify the Moon rather than moons of other bodies, and lunar is the English adjective. Selene is the Greek goddess of the Moon. One of the earliest depictions of the Moon is a 3000 BC rock carving found in Ireland. By 500 BC, the eighteen-year cycle of lunar eclipses was known. About a century after Christ, Ptolemy determined a reasonably accurate distance to the Moon and its diameter.

The Moon rotates 360° around the Earth in 27.3 days. Because the Earth is rotating around the Sun, it takes 29.5 days to show the same phase. The latter is the synodic period. Because the orbit is elliptical, the Moon's distance from Earth ranges from about 222,000 miles to 252,000 miles. At its closest, the Moon appears ever so slightly larger, and it's called a supermoon if it's a new or full moon.

The Moon's phases are not caused by the Earth's shadow, as some believe, but because of the Sun and Moon's relative position. Imagine the Sun is behind you when you look at the Moon. The Moon is fully illuminated. This happens when the Sun is setting as the Moon is rising, or vice versa. Now imagine the Sun is in a similar direction

Wikimedia Commons: NASA DSCOVR satellite: Public domain

as the Moon, but behind the Moon. Then, the Sun illuminates only the far side of the Moon, and the Moon appears dark to us. The inner planets Mercury and Venus also display phases.

Here is a picture of the Earth and Moon from the artificial satellite DSCOVR. This satellite is parked about one million miles from Earth and is used to measure the Solar wind. The Sun is behind the satellite, and the Sun fully illuminates both the Earth and Moon. The Moon looks dark in this photograph because it reflects less light than the Earth. The Moon is actually about the color of aged asphalt. The Moon looks bright in our night sky because the sky is black.

The Moon's mass is about 7.34×10^{22} kilograms, while the Earth's mass is about 5.97×10^{24} kilograms, or 81 times more massive. The Moon does not orbit about the center of the Earth. The Moon and the center of the Earth rotate around a point roughly a thousand miles beneath the Earth's surface. Imagine two ice skaters holding hands, leaning back from each other, and spinning. They rotate about a point between them. If the Moon were even more massive, the rotation point would move away from the Earth and into the space between them.

The Moon's rotational period locks with its orbital period around the Earth. As a consequence, we only see one side of the Moon. The far side of the Moon was seen by human eyes first by Frank Borman, William Anders, and James Lovell from Apollo 8 in December of 1968. Actually, the Moon wobbles a little. Therefore, we can view about

59% of the lunar surface at one time or another. The wobble is caused by the influence of the elliptical orbit on the rotational lock. This movement is called libation, not to be confused with liquid libation, which can also cause the Moon to wobble.

The Moon's Formation

How did the Moon form? Why is it larger than other planetary moons relative to the host planet? Despite the fact they have 10.6 ounces of rock from three Soviet Luna spacecraft, 420 pounds of Lunar meteorites, and 842 pounds of samples from Apollo, scientists haven't reached a consensus on a formation theory. It's agreed that the Moon formed about 4.4 to 4.5 billion years ago, relatively soon after the Solar System itself.

One theory is a blob of the forming Earth split off, but that theory requires the Earth spin was faster than is believed. Another theory suggests the Earth captured a previous formed Moon, but it's not believed the Earth's atmosphere was extensive enough to slow the incoming body. A third theory is that both originated from a similar portion of the early Solar System disk, but the Moon has less metal than the Earth. None of these theories seem to jive with the existing angular momentum of the Earth-Moon system.

The most popular theory is that a massive body collided with the Earth, blasting vast amounts of material from each into Earth orbit. This material gravitationally gathered into the Moon. Many scientists either currently accept this theory or are agnostic.

The Tides

The Sun and Moon both cause the tides of the sea. Remember, gravity decreases with distance. In the figure, the Moon's gravity is pulling on the sea closest to the Moon with force A. It's also pulling on the Earth's center with force B. Since the ocean is closer, it pulls the water with more force and away from the Earth. There is a high tide

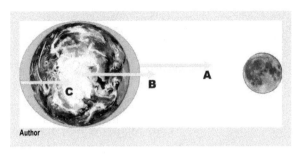
Author

when the Moon is overhead. The Moon is also pulling on the sea on the other side of the Earth with force C. But it pulls the Earth with force B, which is stronger than C, so the tide rises on the far side of the Earth as well. As the Earth rotates, we experience high tides twice daily. If the ocean's depths were constant, and there were no landmasses, nor wind and weather, then the Moon's high tide would raise the sea 21 inches.

The Sun also causes tides, but the Sun only raises the sea about 10 inches due to its increased distance. When the Sun and Moon are on the same or opposite sides of the Earth, these effects add together, and the sea rises about 31 inches. This is called a Spring tide and happens during full and new Moons. When the Moon is pulling in one direction, and the Sun is pulling at a right angle, the effects cancel, and the rise is 11 inches. This is referred to as a neap tide. An incoming tide is called a flood tide, and an outgoing tide is called an ebb tide.

It isn't quite that simple because the wind, storms, barometric pressure, the seafloor's shape, and bays all affect the tides. Local tide tables are necessary for each locale. The ellipticity and inclination of the Moon's orbit also affect the numbers. The tides in the Bay of Funday between Nova Scotia and New Brunswick can be 50 feet, while tide extremes near Anchorage, Alaska, can be 40 feet.

Observing the Moon

In his work, *The Starry Messenger*, Galileo wrote, *"It is a beautiful and delightful sight to behold the body of the Moon."* How true, whether you stare at it floating there, or the Moon stares back shining through the trees and lighting your path on otherwise dark nights.

During its formation, the solar system was a violent place. Objects hurled into the forming Earth and its Moon leaving impact craters. The wind, rain, and vegetation erased most of these features on Earth. They remain in plain sight on the Moon, which has no atmosphere.

What do you see when you look at the Moon? Perhaps you see the Man in the Moon, or maybe the Moon Rabbit. Frankly, I have a hard time with the Man in the Moon. I see a giant one-clawed crab. The dark areas that form these features are referred to as Seas or Maria. They formed during a period several hundred million years after the formation of the Moon. Large impact craters filled later with flowing lava. Apollo samples revealed they are basalt. The higher content of metal in the basalt makes the seas appear darker than the lunar highlands.

In this image of the full Moon, north is up, and the Moon's left side is east. Point A in the image marks the Apollo 11 landing site, just on the south edge of the Sea of Tranquility. Point B marks the crater Tycho which is visible with unaided eyes. Notice the rays of debris emanating from Tycho's impact crater. The rays are generally unbroken by other impact craters and cover the seas' surface, suggesting the Tycho impact is recent. Ray samples returned by Apollo 17 indicate the rays are only 108 million years old.

Point C at the southwest edge of the Sea of Serenity is the landing site of Apollo 17, the last Apollo mission. Point D identifies the Copernicus crater, while point E marks the smaller circular Sea of Crises. Point F is the crater Plato, and G marks the Sea of Fertility. How many of these features can you see with

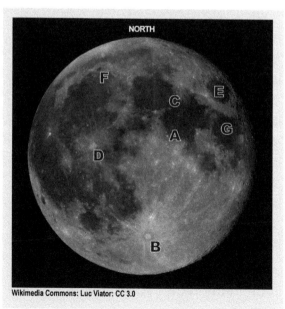

Wikimedia Commons: Luc Viator: CC 3.0

your unaided eyes? Back to the crab. A, C, and G mark the Big Claw. Point D, Copernicus crater is the heart of the crab body. I suppose the Crab in the Moon isn't poetic enough to stick in popular culture, but I want to be remembered for it if it sticks.

Speaking of popular culture, modern media is fixated with supermoons. I think the idea is blown out of proportion to create material for 24-hour networks. The Moon's orbit around the Earth is only slightly elliptical. The difference in appearance when the Moon is close (perigee) isn't a lot different than when it's far. As a testament to the power of media, I'm often asked about supermoons, so here goes.

When the Moon is simultaneously full and closest, it's referred to as a super moon. It originated as an astrological term. During perigee, the Moon appears about 7% larger than average. You likely wouldn't notice unless someone told you. Full moons rise at sunset, and an illusion causes round objects near the horizon to appear larger. This factor perpetuates the hype of super moons. There are twelve or thirteen full Moons each year, and three or four might be supermoons, depending on your definition of how close perigee and full occur. There is no scientific definition. Some supermoons are very slightly more super than others because of factors other than the Moon's eccentricity. I guess that makes them super-duper moons. If this weren't enough, the hype reaches a fever pitch by throwing in a colorful adjective, like wolf or blue. Depending on the season, each full moon has a name, such as a harvest or a hunter's moon. The January full moon is the wolf moon so that you might have a super wolf moon. If a month has two full moons, the second is called a blue moon. There could be a super-blue wolf moon. That only happens once in a blue moon. OK, you get the point.

An interesting lunar phenomenon to observe is Earthshine. When the Moon is less than full, the unlit portion receives no light from the Sun. It would be black, except for the light that reflects off the Earth and shines on the Moon. Earthshine is noticeable only under the right conditions. Clouds reflect more sunlight than the Earth's landmasses. So, when clouds cover a larger portion of

Earth, earthshine is more noticeable. Also, the light from the sunlit part of the Moon is distracting. Earthshine is, therefore, more noticeable during new moons. Daylight is also distracting to earthshine. New moons occur with the Moon appearing nearer the Sun. The newest Moons set soon after the Sun during twilight. The best views of earthshine occur in dark skies, when the Moon is new, and when cloud cover is more extensive than usual. Leonardo da Vinci recognized earthshine for what it was and wrote about it around 1506. It's romantically referred to as *the old Moon in the arms of the new.*

Another fun lunar observation is the Moon as new as possible. The perfectly new, unlit Moon occurs during a solar eclipse, but you can't see the Moon until it begins to cover the Sun's face, so that's cheating. When the Moon is almost in the same direction as the Sun, the Sun's bright light blinds the ability to see an extremely narrow crescent. The best time to catch a really thin crescent at sunset is in late Winter or early Spring when the Moon is higher in the sky at the time of sunset. Internet sources reveal the exact time of a new moon: just type "new moon," the month, and the year. The next sunset after the new moon is the best chance. The world record is about 15 hours after new.

The Telescopic Moon

The Moon is a great first target for your new telescope. The biggest problem novice telescope users face is finding what they want to see, but the Moon isn't hard to find. A modest telescope brings a wealth of interesting features that you can't see with just your eyes. The beginner knows what to expect from pictures, and the results with a small telescope, or even binoculars, are not disappointing. Even light pollution isn't a problem. In fact, the Moon is a fun use of observing time when its light obscures dimmer objects.

It might seem the best time to observe the Moon in a telescope is a full Moon. But during a full Moon, the Sun is directly overhead on the Moon, casting no shadows.

SOUTH

Shadows accentuate details in uneven terrain. Telescopic
views of the Moon are best along the terminator, the region
between night and day on the Moon. As the Moon waxes,
the terminator moves from right to left across the Moon's

face, so the best views move right to left as the month progresses.

This image shows how the Moon appears in a small telescope. A birding scope or 7X50 or larger binoculars reveal a wealth of detail. Many telescopes invert the image of a target, so south is up in this image of the Moon. Birding scopes and binoculars do not invert the image.

Wikimedia Commons: Francisco Villamena: public domain
CHRISTOPHER CLAVIUS
(1538 – 1612) Jesuit German mathematician and astronomer

Point A marks the crater Clavius. Notice the arc of increasingly smaller craters within Clavius. This impressive crater is one of my favorites. Christopher Clavius (1538 – 1612) was a German Jesuit mathematician and astronomer. He was responsible for modifying and promoting the new Gregorian calendar, which we use today. Named after Pope Gregory XIII, the calendar replaced the Julian calendar by changing the year's length to 365.2425 days. This eliminated the drift of the equinoxes on the calendar. Ten days of drift had already occurred over time, so once the new calendar was adopted, October 4, 1582, was followed by October 15, 1582.

Point B is the crater Albategnius, whose western rim was struck later, forming crater Klein. Albategnius is the Latinized form of the Arab astronomer Al-Battani (858 – 929), one of the most influential early Islamic mathematicians and astronomers. This crater is interesting because of the prominent central uplift caused by the impact. Notice how the low Sun to the west lights one side of this uplift mountain and shadows the other.

Point C marks the crater pair Werner and Atiacensis, named after the 15th century Johannes Werner and

Latinized for the French 14th-century theologian Pierre d'Ailly. Notice the proximity of these craters to the terminator causes deep shadows covering much of the crater floor and brightly illuminates the eastern crater rim.

Point D marks Stofler crater, named for a German 15th and 16th-century mathematician and astronomer. This crater is interesting because the crater rim shadows the floor, but the Sun illuminates a central peak.

Notice in the image that impact craters riddle the entire terminator. However, Point E in the Sea of Clouds is almost devoid of craters, suggesting the lunar seas youth relative to most Moon craters.

These features are not unique but exemplify what you can observe on the Moon. As the lunar month waxes and the terminator moves eastward, the changing angle of the Sun causes the appearance of the telescopic Moon to change every day. Enjoy.

Lunar Eclipses

A lunar eclipse occurs when the Moon's orbit brings it into the shadow of the Earth. Eclipses would occur once every month, except the Moon's orbit around the Earth is inclined about 5° to the ecliptic. During a solar eclipse, the Moon's shadow covers only a tiny spot on Earth. To see a solar eclipse, the observer must be on the path the shadow follows. However, during a lunar eclipse, the Earth's shadow covers the entire Moon, so the eclipse is visible to everyone on Earth's night side. For this reason, at a given location on Earth, lunar eclipses are more common than solar eclipses.

Ancients deemed eclipses as omens, typically bad. Over time, a scientific view became prevalent. Prediction of eclipses dates to the time of Christ. In 1503 Columbus, became stranded in Jamaica and short of supplies. The initially friendly natives grew tired of supplying food. Columbus coerced the cooperation of the natives by informing the Chief that the Christian God would become angry and obliterate the Moon (a Lunar eclipse) if the natives did not continue to supply food. Sure enough, as the Moon began to darken, the natives came running with provisions.

Within the umbra portion of the Earth's shadow, no part of the Sun's surface is visible from the Moon. In the penumbra shadow, the Earth covers only a portion of the Sun's surface. However, the atmosphere surrounding the Earth refracts light even into the umbra. If you stood on the Moon during a lunar eclipse and looked back at the Earth, the Earth's atmosphere would be a bright ring of red light. You would observe a "sunset" circling the entire Earth. That red light illuminates the Moon, which is therefore dark red during the eclipse.

In the diagram, most of the Moon is within the umbra, but the edge is within the penumbra. Three types of lunar eclipses occur. If the

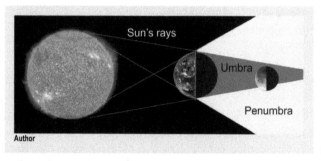

Moon is entirely within the umbra, it's a total eclipse. If a portion of the Moon is in the umbra and a part is in the penumbra, it's a partial eclipse. If the Moon passes through only the penumbra, it's a penumbral eclipse.

The table lists upcoming lunar eclipses. UTC is Coordinated Universal Time as described in the second chapter. The Moon is full just before and after an eclipse. Therefore the Sun is in the exact opposite direction during an eclipse. If the eclipse occurs near local midnight, then the entire duration of the eclipse can be observed. The maximum duration of lunar eclipses is about four hours. In the table, eclipses with maximums at UTC between 1:30 and 8:30 UTC should be visible for the entire duration in the United States. Eclipses between 10:30 and 23:30 are poor times for observing in the United States.

DATE	UTC	TYPE	DATE	UTC	TYPE
Jul 5 2020	4:30	Penumbral	Mar 3 2026	11:33	Total
Nov 30 2020	9:43	Penumbral	Aug 28 2026	4:13	Partial
May 26 2021	11:19	Total	Feb 20 2027	23:13	Penumbral
Nov 19 2021	9:03	Partial	Jul 18 2027	7:14	Penumbral
May 16 2022	4:11	Total	Aug 17 2027	16:03	Penumbral
Nov 8 2022	10:59	Total	Jan 12 2028	4:13	Partial
May 5 2023	17:23	Penumbral	Jul 6 2028	18:19	Partial
Oct 28 2023	20:14	Partial	Dec 31 2028	16:52	Total
Mar 25 2024	7:13	Penumbral	Jun 26 2029	3:22	Total
Sep 18 2024	2:44	Partial	Dec 20 2029	22:42	Total
Mar 14 2025	6:59	Total	Jun 15 2030	18:33	Partial
Sep 7 2025	18:12	Total	Dec 9 2030	22:27	Penumbral

Solar Eclipses

A solar eclipse occurs when the Moon passes in front of the Sun for a viewer on Earth. Because the Earth is just under four times the Moon's size, the Earth appears four times larger from the Moon than the Moon appears from the Earth. The larger Earth can cast a shadow over the entire Moon during a lunar eclipse. However, from the Earth, the Sun and Moon are similar in size. Even though the difference in distance to the Moon during perigee and apogee is small, during perigee, the Moon appears slightly larger than the Sun, while during apogee, the Moon appears slightly smaller.

In this image, the Moon is ever so slightly larger than the Sun, and the Sun's direct surface is totally blocked, resulting in a total eclipse. In this beautiful photograph, red

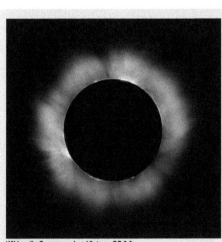

Wikimedia Commons: Luc Viatour: CC 3.0

solar prominences, or flares, are visible. These are eruptions from violent storms near the solar surface. The bright glare of the Sun normally hides the solar corona, the outmost portion of the Sun's atmosphere. This enhanced photograph shows the corona more vividly, but the corona is visible during a total eclipse.

When the Moon is nearer to apogee, the lunar disk is too small to cover the Sun's surface, forming a bright solar ring at the eclipse maximum, called an annular eclipse. Partial eclipses result when the Moon's path doesn't cross the Sun's center. As the Moon's shadow travels across the Earth's surface, the Earth is also rotating. This may take the spot closer or further from the Moon. Rarely an eclipse may transition from annular to total or total to annular. Some observers see a total eclipse, and others see an annular eclipse, resulting in a hybrid eclipse. Because of the Earth's and Moon's movements, the lunar shadow makes a path across the Earth's surface. The maximum path width of totality is 166 miles at lunar perigee, but it's usually narrower. During a total solar eclipse, either side of the path is a partial eclipse.

The table gives total and annual eclipses during the 2020 decade. MAG, or magnitude, refers to the relative apparent size of the Moon to the Sun during the eclipse. A magnitude value of 1 means the Moon and Sun are the same apparent size. The smallest magnitude of an annular eclipse occurring at lunar apogee is about 0.92. Magnitudes less than 0.92 are partial eclipses. The largest possible magnitude occurring at lunar perigee is about 1.08. Larger magnitudes result in longer eclipse durations.

The Moon's surface is mountainous. Just before totality, small areas of light peek through mountain valleys on the Moon, resulting in Baily's beads, named after Francis Baily (1774 – 1844), who described the reason in 1836. It may appear as an arc of a ring

Wikimedia Commons: Tomruen: CC 4.0

with a bright spot, referred to as the diamond ring. These effects may be observed at the beginning and end of totality.

The fact that the Sun and Moon are of similar apparent size is a gift to science. For one thing, it helps scientists study the corona. Einstein's Theory of Relativity predicts that light is bent by a massive object twice as much as Newton's law predicts. Einstein calculated how much the massive Sun should bend starlight. The closer the star appears to the Sun, the more the bending. The deflection is maddingly slight, and the bright Sun's glare dims any hope of observing stars in the direction of the Sun except during an eclipse. During the eclipse of 1919, Arthur Eddington (1882 – 1944) and colleagues led expeditions to Brazil and the island of Principe off Africa's coast. Einstein's calculations proved to be correct.

Observing Solar Eclipses

The experience of a total eclipse is awesome. Partial eclipses are fun, but they don't match the wonder of a total eclipse. The Sun is 400,000 times brighter than the full Moon. That means a partial eclipse covering 95% of the Sun's disk is still 20,000 times brighter than the full Moon. You'll notice the dimming, even as the Moon covers a smaller portion of the Sun. But what strikes you is when Bailey's beads appear, totality follows, it gets very dark, the birds settle, and your friends gasp. The words "life-changing" are perhaps a little strong, but the word "magical" isn't strong enough.

So how do you view an eclipse? First of all, never look directly at the Sun. You can look during totality, but not with optical aid, and be prepared to look away quickly. The lens of your eye will concentrate Sunlight and quite quickly burn the retina. Inexpensive Solar eclipse glasses are available on Amazon and other online sources. These glasses may be paper or plastic and resemble 3-D movie glasses. Never combine eclipse glasses and optical aid. You may use a welder's helmet lens available at local welder supply houses, provided the shade rating is #14 or higher.

DATE	TYPE	MAG	LOCATION
Dec 14 2020	Total	1.025	Polynesia, S.Chile & S.Argentina
Jun 10 2021	Annular	0.943	N.Canada, Greenland, Russia
Dec 4 2021	Total	1.037	Antarctica
Apr 20 2023	Hybrid	1.013	Indonesia, Australia, Papua New Guinea
Oct 14 2023	Annular	0.953	W.US, Central America, Columbia, Brazil
Apr 8 2024	Total	1.057	Mexico, Cental & NE US, E.Canada
Oct 2 2024	Annular	0.933	S.Chile, S.Argentina
Feb 17 2026	Annular	0.963	Antarctica
Aug 12 2026	Total	1.039	Arctic, Greenland, Iceland, Spain
Feb 6 2027	Annular	0.928	Chile, Argentina, Atlantic
Aug 2 2027	Total	1.079	Spain, N.Africa, Yemen, Saudi Arabia
Jan 26 2028	Annular	0.921	Ecuador, Peru, Brazil, Spain, Portugal
Jul 22 2028	Total	1.056	Australia, New Zealand
Jun 1 2030	Annular	0.944	N.Africa, Greece, Turkey, Russia, N.China, Japan
Nov 25 2030	Total	1.047	Botswana, South Africa, Australia

Close one eye and place the lens close and directly over the other eye before looking toward the Sun.

The safest method is to project an image with binoculars. Carefully focus the binoculars on a distant object such as a cloud or most distant tree. Then hold a sheet of paper about a foot behind the binoculars while pointing the binoculars at the Sun. With practice and careful alignment, you'll see images of the Sun projected onto the paper. Again, never attempt to use Solar glasses or a welder's lens combined with binoculars or a telescope.

Another popular way to view an eclipse is with a pinhole lens. Place a pinhole in the middle of a sheet of paper. Hold the paper perpendicular to the Sun and place another paper sheet about two feet behind the pinhole sheet. The pinhole projects an image of the Sun onto the second sheet. As a boy, during my first solar eclipse, I happened to look down and see crescents in the

Author

partial shade of a nearby tree. In places, gaps between the leaves in the tree form small holes for the sunlight to shine through, creating many pinhole lenses. The image here is a photograph of light shining through a tree onto the ground, taken just before totality during the solar eclipse of August 21, 2017.

Apollo

Any story about the Earth's moon isn't complete without the story of men setting foot on it. John F. Kennedy's (1917 - 1963) clear challenge delivered to Congress on May 25, 1961, was: *"First, I believe that this nation should commit itself to achieving the goal, before this decade is out, of landing a man on the moon and returning him safely to the earth."* Congress approved, and 400,000 men and women went to work to make it happen.

A stunned United States was furiously trying to catch up in the space race after Russia launched the first artificial Earth satellite, Sputnik I, on October 4, 1957. When I visited the University of Illinois Engineering Open House as a middle schooler, the constant beeping of Sputnik I played over a campus loudspeaker. I started a scrapbook of newspaper clippings of failed US Vanguard rocket launches and the space race. The US finally launched Explorer 1 into orbit on January 31, 1958. Then Yuri Gagarin (1934 – 1968) orbited Earth onboard Vostok 1 in April of 1961. But the US was making progress. Twenty days before Kennedy's challenge, Alan Shepard (1923 – 1998) made a suborbital flight into space.

The National Aeronautics and Space Administration was formed earlier in 1958. NASA advanced its plans, technology, and equipment using three different crew systems. Project Mercury used a single-man Earth-orbiting capsule. Project Gemini used a two-man capsule to advance rendezvous, docking, and extravehicular activity (EVA). Apollo used a three-man command module.

Wikimedia Commons: NASA astronaut William Anders: public domain

It was going well until the crew of Apollo 1, Gus Grissom, Ed White, and Roger Chaffee, died during an otherwise routine but tragic test at the launch pad on January 27, 1967. NASA reevaluated the program and redesigned the Apollo command module. The first crewed flight was Apollo 7, launched on October 11, 1968. Apollo 8 launched December 21, 1968, and Frank Borman, Jim Lovell, and Bill Anders circled the Moon taking this iconic image on Christmas eve, 1968. Called Earthrise, it gave a new perspective of mankind's place in the universe.

The Apollo Spacecraft

This illustration depicts to scale of the three NASA space capsules and their launch vehicles on a smaller scale. The Apollo spacecraft included three systems. The Command module held the three astronauts during much of the mission, including launch and reentry. Attached behind the Command module is the Service module. It included propulsion, electrical systems, and consumables. As an assembly, these two components were called the Command Service Module, or CSM. The CSM was developed and built for NASA by North American Aviation beginning in 1961. On the right of the Apollo spacecraft is the Lunar Excursion Module or LEM. Grumman Aircraft managed the LEM development. It was too fragile to withstand launch through the Earth's atmosphere, and an enclosing shroud protected it during launch.

Lunar missions began with about eleven minutes of burn by the massive three-stage Saturn V rocket to put the Apollo spacecraft and top third stage of the rocket into

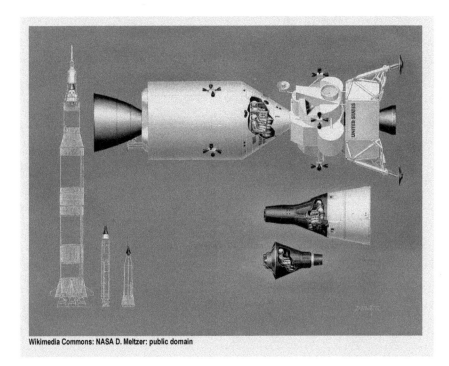

Wikimedia Commons: NASA D. Meltzer: public domain

Earth orbit. After one or two orbits of the Earth to check out systems, the third stage of the Saturn V reignited to place the spacecraft on a trajectory toward the Moon, that is, where the Moon would be in three days. During the launch, the fragile LEM was behind the CSM and protected by a shroud. On the way to the Moon, the shroud panels jettisoned, the CSM separated, and then it turned around to dock with the LEM. The illustration depicts the docked position. The docked spacecrafts then backed away from the third stage. They coasted the rest of the way to the Moon with minor midcourse corrections when necessary.

The trajectory caused the spacecraft to loop behind the Moon. Behind the Moon, the Service module engine fired to slow the spacecraft into a lunar orbit. In early missions, if the Service module engine failed to fire, the spacecraft would loop around the Moon and return to Earth. After a rest, the mission commander and the LEM pilot entered the LEM through the docking collar and powered up the LEM. The LEM crew then backed away from the CSM and briefly fired the descent engine. As the LEM approached the lunar surface, the descent engine fired again for a powered landing.

After missions on the surface, the ascent engine fired using the descent stage on the illustration's far-right as a launchpad. The ascent stage achieved lunar orbit and rendezvoused with the CSM. The LEM crew reentered the CSM and joined the command module pilot.

They then jettisoned the LEM and crashed it into the Moon. Seismographs left on the Moon recorded the crash to study the internal structure of the Moon.

The CSM engine fired a final time to place the CSM in an Earth-bound trajectory. Approaching Earth, the crew jettisoned the Service module and turned the command module's blunt end toward the atmosphere for reentry. Harrison Schmitt took this image of Eugene Cernan standing on the Moon during the last manned lunar mission, Apollo 17. Talk about a beautiful view of the Moon. Imagine the view these fellows saw.

Saturn V

Central to the success of the Apollo program was the massive Saturn V rocket. NASA realized immediately that landing on the Moon would require a huge heavy-lift rocket vehicle. Before Kennedy's challenge, the development of a series of Saturn rockets began as a follow-up to the successful Jupiter series of rockets. The Saturn V consisted of a Boeing S-IC first stage with five Rocketdyne F-1 engines burning highly-refined kerosene and liquid oxygen. The North American Aviation S-II second stage used five Rocketdyne J-2 engines burning liquid hydrogen and liquid oxygen. The Douglas Aircraft S-IVB third stage used one J-2 engine, also burning liquid hydrogen and liquid oxygen. As they burned, the second and third stages left behind a trail of pure steam.

The Saturn V first launched in November of 1967. It produced over 7,500,000 pounds of thrust and could put 310,000 pounds into Earth orbit and launch 107,000 pounds toward the Moon. No rocket has ever been built that was as powerful, including the Space Shuttle. The Space Shuttles' total thrust of the three main engines and the two attached solid rocket boosters was about 6,800,000 pounds of thrust.

Werner Von Braun was the first director of the Marshall Space Flight Center, and the chief architect of the Saturn V. His interest in rocketry for space flight began as a boy. Later, he led the development at the German seaport of Peenemunde, the V-2 rocket used to terrorize London during World War II. In May 1945, to avoid being captured by the Soviets, Von Braun carefully maneuvered his team of 450 to 500 men so the Americans would capture them. The Americans also captured V-2s. Later, Von Braun continued rocket research in the US for the Army using the captured V-2s. This photo of Von Braun standing beside the Saturn V engines reveals the size of the giant machine that sent men to the Moon.

Wikimedia Commons: NASA: public domain

WERNER VON BRAUN
(1912 - 1977) Early rocket engineer and director of the Marshall Space Flight Center

Now, let's leave the Moon and explore more distant solar system bodies, at least by words, pictures, and your imagination.

5 The Solar System

The Sun reigns over a complex system of objects other than just the eight planets. Don't worry, Pluto, I won't leave you out. Most of the planets are systems themselves, with objects orbiting around them. But indeed, the Sun reigns with a mass of 99.86% of the entire system. Everything orbits around the Sun. Well, almost. A few objects pass through once and leave the solar system.

The Solar System

The solar system is a collection of objects gravitationally bound to the massive Sun. It consists of eight planets, five currently recognized dwarf planets, many moons orbiting these objects, millions of asteroids, comets, Kuiper belt objects, and the Oort Cloud. Beginning early in the 19th century, the names of objects other than planets and comets changed to minor planets. But as the number of minor planets discovered ballooned, groups of unique categories were given names, such as asteroids, dwarf planets, centaurs, Kuiper belt objects, trojans, and more. Into which category an object fell became more a matter of definition than fundamental differences.

The former planet Pluto can attest to this mess. In 2006, the International Astronomical Union (IAU) reclassified Pluto from a planet to a dwarf planet. They had their reasons, including the fact that a similar object, Eris, which is even larger than Pluto, was discovered in 2005. Nevertheless, I'll never forgive the IAU. Since childhood, I'd learned about the nine planets. I could have dealt with the discovery of more planets, but taking one away, never! That's off my chest, so as we explore the solar system, I'll write about the new categories.

Solar System Formation

The Copernican revolution, the observation by Galileo that moons orbit Jupiter, and the concept that gravity attracts mass led the brilliant French Renaissance thinker Pierre-Simon Laplace, continuing the work of others, to propose in 1796 a basic theory about the formation of the solar system.

Wikimedia Commons: J. Posselwhite: public domain
PIERRE-SIMON LAPLACE
(1749 - 1827) Great French mathematician, astronomer, engineer, and philosopher

Our galaxy, the Milky Way, contains not only billions of stars but vast clouds of gas, much of which is molecular hydrogen. About 4.6 billion years ago, one of these clouds began a slow collapse due to its gravity. Like spinning ice skaters who fold their arms, initial swirling in the cloud sped up as the cloud collapsed. As gravity continued the collapse, much of the mass gravitated near the center and became hotter. The center continued to become hotter and denser from the collapse. After millions of years, the nebulous cloud had collapsed to a dense and sufficiently hot mass that hydrogen began to fuse. The nuclear fusion pressure pushed outward, stopping the gravitational collapse, and the Sun was born. The spinning caused the matter to flatten into a disk. At the time fusion began, not all of the disk had collapsed into the center. Gravity within local swirls began collecting the material into planets. This slow gravitational collection of all the material in an orbital zone into a single body is called accretion.

The inner solar system's temperature was high enough to boil off volatile gases, and the inner planets became rocky. Farther out, the Sun's heat was insufficient to boil away the collected gas of giant planets. The lower abundance of heavier elements in the original cloud resulted in the smaller size of the rocky planets.

The Sun

The Sun is not the simple hot-yellow ball it might seem to be. Being gaseous, it has no surface in the usual sense. The visual surface, or photosphere, defines the Sun's diameter. Its diameter is about 864,000 miles or 109 times that of Earth. Above the photosphere are multiple layers with different properties. One of the layers, the corona, is visible during total solar eclipses when light from brighter, lower Sun layers is blocked. For reasons only partly understood, some of the upper layers are much hotter than layers close to the Sun.

This photograph of the Sun was taken at ultraviolet wavelengths but recolored to orange, so it is visible. In this image, many atmospheric features of the Sun are visible. Convection currents in the hot ionized gases called plasma cause surface granulation. Mass ejections of plasma, called prominences, can be seen extending outward from the Sun's photosphere.

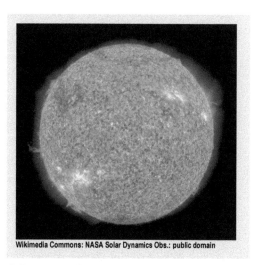
Wikimedia Commons: NASA Solar Dynamics Obs.: public domain

The strong magnetic fields of the Sun often cause these prominences to form loops that return to the Sun. The lighter areas in this image are the prominences' bases viewed more directly rather than from the side. These features are visible with specialized solar telescopes available for $600 to $4000.

The mass of the Sun is 330,000 times that of Earth. The Sun contains roughly 99.86% of the mass of the Solar system. That mass is 73% hydrogen, 25% helium, and the remaining two percent is primarily oxygen, carbon, neon, and iron.

Scientists realized early that chemical burning could not produce the energy released by the Sun. The British astronomer and mathematician Arthur Eddington (1882 – 1944), in a 1920 technical paper, first suggested the Sun released energy by fusing hydrogen into helium. In a simplified model, the atom's nucleus consists of positively charged protons and neutral neutron particles of similar mass. Together they are called nucleons. The number of protons in the nucleus defines each element's physical and chemical properties and is called the atomic number. Hydrogen with an atomic number of one is the simplest element with one proton and no neutrons. Helium has two protons and two neutrons with an atomic number of two.

It would seem, if you took the weight of each atom and divided it by the quantity of nucleons, it would be the weight of a single nucleon. But something amazing happens. The weight per nucleon of elements with moderate atomic numbers is less than that of the elements with either low or high atomic numbers. That means if you fuse hydrogen atoms into helium, there is mass left over. It also means if you split a very heavy atom into two lighter atoms, again, there is mass left over. The process of splitting atoms is called fission, and it's how nuclear power plants produce energy. The process of fusing elements is called fusion, and it's how the hydrogen bomb works and how the Sun produces energy. Einstein's famous equation $E=mc^2$ predicts the energy released by the converted mass. The velocity of light, c, is a big number, and squaring it means a little mass, m, creates a lot of energy, E.

The Sun is a typical-sized star in middle age. Every second, the Sun converts about 9 billion pounds of matter into energy. It has used up about 0.03% of its mass. At this rate, it will continue to burn hydrogen into helium for another 5 billion years. Over this long time frame, the Sun will grow warmer and larger. The current rate is about a 1% increase in brightness every 100 million years. Eventually, its size will extend past the Earth's orbit. It will shrink and grow a few times through various phases of nuclear reactions and ultimately end as a white dwarf.

How is this known? The Sun is a typical star. Our galaxy has billions of stars to study. Small stars, big stars, young stars, old stars all shine light on us, and that light reveals information about the abundance of elements and the temperature of the star. The development of the hydrogen bomb in 1952, theoretical studies, and computer simulations provided a deep understanding of fusion. I'll write more about the life of other stars in the chapter Stars.

Sunspots

Solar activity is variable with time. During periods of higher activity, cooler areas on the surface create visible spots on the Sun. These spots are observable with unaided eyes at the moment of sunset. On totally cloudless days, when the Sun begins setting, the atmosphere protects your eyes. Solar eclipse glasses are safer still. A welder's helmet lens may be used provided the shade rating is #14 or higher. Close one eye and place the lens close and directly over the other eye before looking toward the Sun. The Solar Dynamics Observatory website, *sdo.gsfc.nans.gov*, offers a safe and convenient way to view the Sun.

The temperature of the photosphere within the sunspots is about 6000°F to 7000°F, but because the Sun's temperature is generally about 10,000°F, the sunspots appear dark. The number of sunspots waxes and wanes over roughly eleven years. The spots are associated with solar flares and prominences. During periods with more sunspots, solar radiation is slightly higher. The solar storms associated with these flares can disrupt radio communications, and when sufficiently strong, can even disrupt electrical power grids. In 1989, a massive flare took down the power grid in Quebec, Canada, and areas were without power for twelve hours. Auroras were seen as far south as Florida to Texas. An even larger solar eruption occurred in 2012, but that flare missed the Earth by about nine days in the Earth's orbit around the Sun.

Wikimedia Commons: Geoff Elston: CC 4.0

The rotational period of the Sun as viewed from the Earth at the Sun's equator is about 28 days. The rotational period near the poles is more like 36 days. This difference is possible because the Sun is gaseous. Sunspots rotate with the surface and disappear off the western edge as we view it and may live long enough to reappear on the eastern edge of the Sun during the next rotation.

The average quantity of sunspots per month has been informally recorded since about 1610 and accurately recorded since 1755. Astronomers numbered sunspots beginning with the 1755 cycle. Cycle 24 started in early 2008 and ended in late 2019. The peak numbers and timing are notoriously challenging to predict, and there is little consensus on the prediction for cycle 25. In this

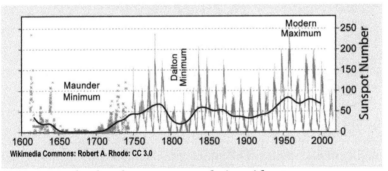

Wikimedia Commons: Robert A. Rhode: CC 3.0

graph, the eleven-year cycle is evident.

The Maunder Minimum was a period from 1650 to 1700 with few observed sunspots. It corresponded to a period of lower temperatures in Europe called the Little Ice Age. A correlation between high sunspot activity and higher solar irradiance, or solar heating, has been confirmed in recent decades. Notice a general trend upward in sunspot activity from 1700 to the present, named the Modern Maximum. The last cycle, 24, had relatively low activity. The Sun is a dynamic system. Longer-term trends are likely. Whether changes in solar activity are responsible for past ice ages and warming trends is uncertain.

The Ecliptic

The ecliptic is the Sun's path through the celestial background. Except for the long-term precession discussed previously, the Earth's rotational axis points in the same direction in relation to the stars as the Earth orbits around the Sun. For Northern Hemisphere observers, during the Earth's nightly rotation, the constellations always peak at the same elevation due south. The rectangular map of the constellations on the next page uses this constant frame of reference. The celestial equator is a straight line through the center of the chart.

Because of the Earth's axial tilt to its orbit around the Sun, the Sun does not follow a path with constant elevation during the seasons. For the Northern Hemisphere, the Sun passes high overhead in the Summer but lower in the winter's southern skies. At night, the reverse is true. The ecliptic is low on Summer nights and high on Winter nights. In the Summer, the constellation Sagittarius is just above the southern horizon for mid-northern latitudes.

As practiced by astrology, beginning with the Babylonians, the ecliptic was divided into twelve equal $30°$ segments of the sky to conform with the twelve-month lunar calendar. Astrologers conveniently ignored that the ecliptic passes through Ophiuchus. The astrological Zodiac's twelve constellations are Aries, Taurus, Gemini, Cancer, Leo, Virgo, Libra, Scorpius, Sagittarius, Capricornus, Aquarius, and Pisces.

If the planets all orbited in the same plane, they too would always lie on the ecliptic. Of the five visible planets, Jupiter is inclined the least to the ecliptic at $1.3°$ and Mercury the most at $7°$. Because the inclinations are slight, the planets always appear near the ecliptic. The planets wander among some 25 constellations. The label colors in this chart indicate the date of the constellation establishment.

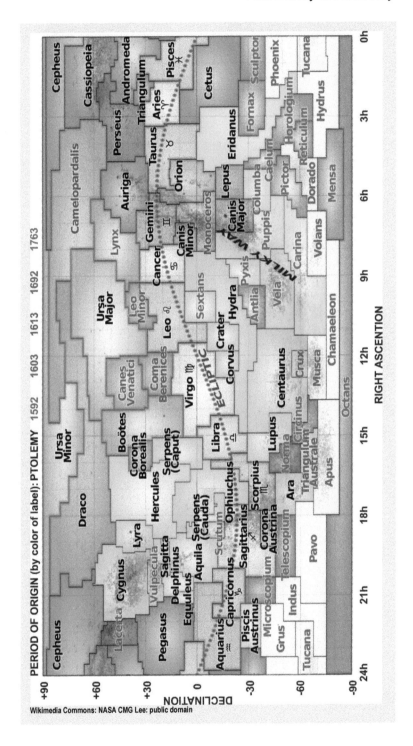

The Planets

The five innermost planets wandered amongst the background stars, and the ancients knew they were different than stars. The term planet was derived from the Greek "planete," which means wanderer. As astronomers discovered more and more solar system bodies, the definition of a planet morphed into fuzziness. In 2006, the IAU adopted the term planet for a body orbiting the Sun that assumed a round shape and cleared its neighborhood of smaller objects. The third requirement was necessary to avoid classifying two of the larger asteroids as planets. This planet classification problem is not new. From 1807 to 1845, astronomers recognized eleven planets with four asteroids as planets. Neptune and Pluto were undiscovered.

I'll reluctantly accept the IAU definition of eight

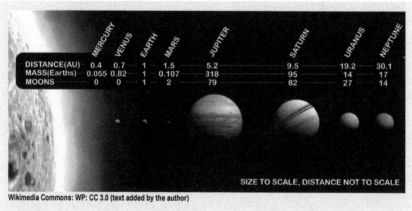

	MERCURY	VENUS	EARTH	MARS	JUPITER	SATURN	URANUS	NEPTUNE
DISTANCE(AU)	0.4	0.7	1	1.5	5.2	9.5	19.2	30.1
MASS(Earths)	0.055	0.82	1	0.107	318	95	14	17
MOONS	0	0	1	2	79	82	27	14

SIZE TO SCALE, DISTANCE NOT TO SCALE

Wikimedia Commons: WP: CC 3.0 (text added by the author)

planets in the solar system. They are illustrated here with the Sun and with their diameters to scale. Their distance from the Sun is not to scale. The diagram gives each planet's mass and distance from the Sun relative to the Earth and the number of each planet's moons. For example, Jupiter is 5.2 times further from the Sun than Earth is from the Sun. These are average numbers because the planet's orbits are elliptical rather than circular, and therefore their distance from the Sun varies. The mass of Jupiter is 318 times that of the Earth. In fact, Jupiter is 2.5 times more massive than all other planets combined.

Jupiter currently has 79 classified moons. When I was a boy, 12 moons of Jupiter were known. Advances in telescopes, astronomical imagery with electronic devices, and space probes have significantly increased the number of moons.

Mercury

Wikimedia Commons: NASA: public domain

MERCURY ☿

Aphelion	0.467 au
Perihelion	0.307 au
Orbital period	87.97 days
Synodic period	115.88 days
Inclination	7°
Diameter	0.383 Earths
Mass	0.055 Earths
Axial tilt	0.034°
Magnitude	-2.48 - 0 7.25
Angular diam	4.5 - 13"

The planet Mercury is the closest planet to the Sun. Its orbital period is the shortest of all the planets, so it wanders rapidly amongst the stellar background. Mercury is named for the fleet-footed Roman god Mercury, the messenger of the gods. Its atmosphere is extremely tenuous, and the mottled surface appearance with impact craters is not unlike the Moon.

The orbital eccentricity is the largest of the planets, as evidenced by the large difference in its distance from the Sun during the closest approach (perihelion) and farthest (aphelion). The orbital period is 87.97 days referenced to the stars and the synodic period as viewed from the orbiting Earth is 115.88 days. The inclination of Mercury's orbit is 7° to the ecliptic. The tilt of the axis of rotation is the smallest of all the planets, 0.034°.

Mercury is an inferior planet which means its orbit is inside the Earth's orbit; therefore, it never wanders far from the Sun. The largest angular separation from the Sun is 28°. Because Mercury is inferior, its disk's apparent angular size varies substantially. Its distance from Earth ranges from about 0.53 to 1.47 au, almost a factor of three. Also, because it's inferior, Mercury has visual phases like the Moon. Because of this, the visual magnitude of Mercury varies widely.

Have you seen Mercury? Many people have not seen Mercury despite the fact it's sometimes quite bright and easy to see. But because it never wanders far from the Sun, you must have a good view of the horizon and pick the time wisely. As Mercury never wanders far from the Sun, it's always a morning "star" or an evening star. It rises not long before the Sun or sets soon after the Sun.

MORNING STAR	EVENING STAR
7/4/2021	1/24/2021
10/25/2021	5/17/2021
1/30/2023	1/7/2022
9/22/2023	4/29/2022
1/12/2024	4/11/2023
9/5/2024	3/24/2024
8/19/2025	3/8/2025
8/2/2026	2/19/2026
7/15/2027	2/3/2027
1/9/2029	5/28/2027
10/1/2029	1/17/2028
1/22/2030	5/9/2028
9/15/2030	4/21/2029
	4/4/2030

The path of the Sun is called the ecliptic, and the Moon and planets follow similar paths. If the ecliptic is perpendicular to the horizon at sunset, and Mercury is at maximum elongation, Mercury will be 28° high. But now imagine the ecliptic is more parallel to the horizon. At its furthest elongation from the Sun, it will not be as high above the horizon. The angle of the ecliptic to the horizon varies during the year. The most favorable ecliptic tilt for seeing Mercury occurs from January to May when Mercury is an evening star and from July to January when it's a morning star. The table shows the dates for the 2020 decade for Mercury's maximum elongation from the Sun and a favorably inclined ecliptic. A week before or after these dates are the best chance to see Mercury. As an evening star, Mercury is brighter when fuller before these dates and dimmer but more of a crescent after these dates. At sunrise, the opposite is true. Soon after sunset and with a clear view of the horizon, look in the direction of the sunset. With a good telescope, you will be able to discern a disk, but you won't be able to see any surface details.

When Mercury passes between the Sun and Earth, if the inclination is correct, Mercury may transit across the face of the Sun. My first view of Mercury was a transit on November 7, 1960. I was a boy of 13 and had purchased a three-inch reflector for $29.95 from Edmund Scientific. The last transit of Mercury was November 11, 2019, and the next is November 13, 2032.

Here are a few tidbits about Mercury. Jupiter's moon Ganymede and Saturn's moon Titan are larger than the planet Mercury. Mercury is closer to the size of our Moon than to that of Earth. Mercury's orbit didn't quite follow Newton's and Kepler's laws of gravity and planetary motion. There was a tiny error discovered as early as 1859. Various proposed solutions didn't solve the mystery. Then in 1915, Einstein explained the error precisely using his General Theory of Relativity. It was one of the first confirmations of his theory. The error was first discovered with Mercury because it's the closest planet to the Sun, whose gravity bends space, and therefore, the error was the largest of the planets. Scientists now know the planets' positions so accurately we can land on them.

Venus

Venus is the second closest planet to the Sun. Since it's inferior, it's also a morning star or an evening star. But it orbits about twice as far from the Sun as Mercury, so its elongation is greater, making it easier to see. It's larger than Mercury and closer to us at times, thus making it much brighter. Other than the Moon, it's the brightest object in the night sky. Its diamond-like color and brightness are beautiful, earning it the name of the Roman god of love and beauty.

It's sometimes referred to as Earth's sister planet because its size, distance from the Sun, and composition are more like Earth's than any other planet. But the similarities end there. It has a dense atmosphere of primarily carbon dioxide with a pressure at the surface 92 times that of Earth. The dense atmosphere obscures any visible surface features and forms a blanket making Venus hotter than Mercury. The surface temperature is over 800°F.

The Soviet Union successfully landed multiple Venera series probes on the planet from 1965 to 1975. Venera 9 returned multiple images showing a debris field with a soil-like surface heavily cluttered with sharp-edged, slab-like rocks. The Soviet Union, United States, European Union, and Japan have also explored Venus with flybys and orbiters. Radar mapping reveals smooth volcanic plains covering large portions of Venus. There are two higher continents. The northern continent is called Ishtar Terra after the Babylonian goddess of love, and the southern is named Aphrodite Terra after the Greek goddess of love.

Wikimedia Commons: NASA: public domain

VENUS ♀

Aphelion	0.728 au
Perihelion	0.718 au
Orbital period	224.7 days
Synodic period	583.9 days
Inclination	3.39°
Diameter	0.95 Earths
Mass	0.816 Earths
Axial tilt	2.64°
Magnitude	-4.92 – 2.98
Angular diam	9.7 to 66"

These are the dates of Venus's greatest elongation from the Sun as a morning star and an evening star. Because Venus takes longer than Mercury to orbit the Sun, it wanders amongst the stars more slowly. Venus is a stunning morning and evening star for two months on either side of these dates.

Observing the crescent of Venus is a good test of your binocular and observing skills. It's bright, so Venus is easy to spot and good practice for holding and finding objects in the binoculars. Venus appears as a thin crescent one month before these dates when a morning star and one month after these dates when an evening star. With high-quality 7x50 binoculars, you should be able to discern a crescent barely. It will be easier with 10x50 or larger binoculars. You'll need to steady the binoculars by resting them on a post or the side of a tree. Almost all binoculars use short focal-length achromats, so you will see significant false-color distortions in Venus. But still, it's fun to

MORNING STAR	EVENING STAR
3/20/2022	10/29/2021
10/23/2023	6/4/2023
6/1/2025	1/10/2025
1/3/2027	8/15/2026
8/10/2028	3/22/2028
3/17/2030	10/27/2029

know you've seen Venus as a crescent.

Observing Venus in daylight is possible if you know exactly where to look. The best approach is first to view it as a morning star and follow it as it rises. Observing Venus during the day is easy in a telescope if you can find it. Finding planets during the day is one example of the usefulness of more advanced go-to telescopes.

Like Mercury, but not nearly as often, Venus transits the Sun's disk. Transits occur in pairs about eight years apart. The last pair was in June of 2004 and 2012. The next pair are in December of 2117 and 2125. Don't worry; you won't miss them. These transits will be in the news.

Mars

Wikimedia Commons: ESA: CC 3.0

MARS ♂

Aphelion	1.666 au
Perihelion	1.382 au
Orbital period	686.97 days
Synodic period	779.96 days
Inclination	1.85°
Diameter	0.533 Earths
Mass	0.107 Earths
Axial tilt	25.19°
Magnitude	-2.94 – 1.86
Angular diam	3.5 – 25.1"
Moons	2

Mars, named after the Roman god of war, is the fourth planet from the Sun. Iron oxide in Mars's soil causes the red color. The thin atmosphere doesn't protect the surface from meteorites, and the current lack of flowing water results in numerous craters. Once more active, Mars posses plains, valleys, mountains, and polar ice caps. There are two small and irregularly shaped moons; Phobos and Deimos.

Mars's distance from the Sun varies from 1.382 to 1.666 au. Its diameter is about half that of Earth, and its mass is only 11% of Earth's. Its axial tilt is similar to Earth, and as a consequence, it has seasons, although because its orbital period is twice that of Earth's, its seasons are twice as long. The temperature varies from about -225°F in the Winter at the poles to a maximum of 95°F at the equator. The extremes are due to the thin atmosphere's inability to act like a blanket.

The atmosphere has an average surface pressure of about 0.6% of that of Earth. It's 96% carbon dioxide, with just under 2% each of argon and nitrogen, and traces of water vapor and oxygen. Mars has occasional dust storms that reach up to 100 miles per hour. They can be regional or encompass the entire planet. The low atmospheric pressure precludes any liquid surface water, although the polar ice caps store vast amounts of water.

Because Mars has seasons with polar ice caps that wax and wane, and a length of day similar to Earth, there was speculation about life on Mars. William Whewell (1794 – 1866), an English polymath, scientist, Anglican priest, and philosopher, gave the idea credence. He was an influential Master at Trinity College and coined the term scientist. In 1854, he theorized there were seas, land, and possibly life on Mars. Percival Lowell (1855 – 1916) used the famous 24-inch refractor at Lowell Observatory at Flagstaff, Arizona, to draw sketches of Mars with canals, and published three books from 1895 to 1908. Speculation about life on Mars reached a fever pitch. Some astronomers were skeptical from the start. Later observation with larger telescopes cast further doubt, and Lowell's canals eventually dried up in the scientific opinion. The canals were an illusion, but the search for life on Mars goes on.

Mars has two small moons, Phobos and Deimos. Both were discovered in 1877 by the American astronomer Asaph Hall (1829 – 1907). He used the largest refractor in the world at the time, the 26-inch at the US Naval Observatory in Washington, DC. Viewing them requires large amateur telescopes and is an advanced challenge.

Observing Mars

The red appearance of Mars, and its brightness, make it easy to spot at favorable times. Because the orbits of the planets Venus and Mars are adjacent to the Earth, when all three are in the same direction from the Sun, we are closest to them in a geometry called opposition. When Venus or

Wikimedia Commons: NASA:
public domain

Mars is in the same direction as the Sun, it's called a conjunction. Mars is about seven times closer to Earth during opposition than during conjunction, causing a significant difference in the brightness and the disk size when viewed through a telescope. With amateur telescopes, the polar ice caps are only visible near opposition.

This table lists recent and future Mars oppositions. Even though these dates are all oppositions, Mars is closer during some oppositions than others because both the Earth's and Mars's orbits are elliptical. Column two of the table gives the distance at the opposition date. The third column is the apparent diameter in arcseconds as viewed from Earth. Near opposition, Mars is discernable as a disk in small telescopes. This image is how Mars might appear in a larger amateur telescope during opposition. The fourth column is the constellation that Mars is in during opposition.

DATE	DIST(au)	SIZE(")	CONST
7/27/2018	0.3850	24.3	Capricornus
10/13/2020	0.4149	22.6	Pisces
12/8/2022	0.5445	17.2	Taurus
1/16/2025	0.6423	14.6	Gemini
2/19/2027	0.6779	13.8	Leo
3/25/2029	0.6472	14.5	Virgo
5/4/2031	0.5534	16.9	Libra
6/27/2033	0.4230	22.1	Sagittarius
9/15/2035	0.3804	24.6	Aquarius

During opposition, as you view Mars, the Sun is directly behind you. At midnight, the Sun is shining overhead on the other side of the Earth, and Mars is south. During opposition, Mars rises around sunset, sets around sunrise, and is therefore visible all night. Mars may not be exactly south at midnight because of daylight savings time and the effects of local mean time.

A month or two on either side of these dates affords good viewing for Mars. As it orbits the Sun, each night, Mars is a little further eastward among the stars. However, Earth orbits the Sun more quickly than Mars. Earth begins to overtake Mars near opposition. About a month before opposition, Mars slows and pauses its eastward drift among the stars. It then begins a westward drift and continues to do so during opposition and for about a month. This movement reversal is called retrograde motion and is why early astronomers devised epicycles.

Asteroids

In the 18th century, Genevan Charles Bonnet (1720 – 1793) noted a pattern in the planets' distance from the Sun, now referred to as the Titus-Bode Law. It seems rather arbitrary, but it works. Consider the numerical series 0, 3, 6, 12, 24, 48, 96, etc. Adding four to each number and dividing by 10 results in astronomical units of 0.4, 0.7, 1.0, 1.6, 2.8, 5.2, 10, etc. Mercury is 0.4, Venus is 0.6, Earth is 1.0, Mars is 1.6, and Jupiter is 5.2, and Saturn is 10. What is the planet for 2.8? Kepler wrote, *"between Mars and Jupiter, I place a planet."* Then the German-born British astronomer William Hershel (1738 – 1822) discovered Uranus, which nearly fit the law at 19.6, so a search began for the planet at 2.8 au.

The first discovery was Ceres in 1801 by the Italian priest and astronomer Giuseppe Piazzi (1746 – 1826). Astronomers initially classified Ceres as a planet. Ceres is a spherical asteroid with a diameter of 580 miles. NASA's Dawn spacecraft orbited and mapped Ceres in detail in 2015 and took this photograph.

After discovering Ceres, astronomers discovered Pallas in 1802, Juno in 1804, and Vesta in 1807. Asteroid discoveries became regular after 1845, and they lost their classification as planets and became asteroids, named for "star-like, star-shaped" in Greek. By 1868 over 100 had been discovered, 1,000 by 1921, 10,000 by 1989, 100,000 by 2005, and over 1,000,000 by 2020!

One estimate is that there are 1.1 to 1.9 million

Wikimedia Commons: NASA Justin Cowart: public domain

asteroids at least 0.6 miles in diameter, and many more that are smaller. They are dispersed in space around the Sun, shaped like a donut with the middle of the torus having a diameter closer to Mars than Jupiter. Despite many asteroids, the total mass is a fraction of our Moon, and the density is relatively low. Numerous space probes have passed through the belt with no collisions.

As observed in telescopes, asteroids do appear star-like. Even the brightest, Ceres, about magnitude seven at its brightest, is too dim to see with the unaided eye, even in dark skies. It's viewable with small telescopes and even binoculars, but it's a more suitable task for those with observing experience. The challenge is two-fold; knowing where to look and discerning it from similar-looking stars. Go-to telescopes make this much easier. Otherwise, the best approach is to use those nights near opposition when it's brightest and passing by a more easily located object.

OPPOSITION	CONJUNCTION	OBJECT	RETRO TIMING
8/28/2020		0.06° S. of NGC7492	After
11/27/2021	11/2/2021	0.1° S. of Aldebaran	During
3/21/2023	3/9/2023	0.04° NE of M91	During
7/6/2024	7/15/2024	0.7° N. of M54	During
10/2/2025			
1/7/2027	1/11/2027	0.2° NW of s Gemini	During
5/5/2028			
8/10/2029	11/30/2029	1.2° S. of M30	After

The first column in this table gives the opposition dates. The second column shows the date Jupiter passes by a more easily located object. The third column gives the closest approach in degrees from the listed object. Later chapters provide descriptions of these objects. The final column indicates the timing of the nearest pass in relation to retrograde motion. "During" signifies the pass occurs during Ceres retrograde motion among the stellar background.

Jupiter

Jupiter is named for the Roman king of the gods and the god of the sky and thunder. Only the Sun, the Moon, and the planet Venus outshine Jupiter, the fifth planet from the Sun. Jupiter is the largest planet in the Solar system, at 11 times the diameter and 318 times the Earth's mass. In fact, the mass of Jupiter is 2.5 times that of the rest of the planets combined. But Jupiter is not a rock. Like the other outer planets, it's gas. Jupiter's mass is about 71% hydrogen, 24% helium, and small amounts of a dozen other elements. Because it's gas and rotates in just under 10 hours, the fastest rotation of any planet, it bulges slightly at the equator.

Jupiter isn't a pleasant place to picnic. Jupiter's storms are violent, with winds usually above 100 miles per hour. One cyclone, the Great Red Spot, is larger than the Earth, is visible in amateur telescopes, and has been brewing for centuries. Lightning storms a hundred times stronger than those on Earth rage in the atmosphere of Jupiter. Beneath the visible upper atmosphere may be water clouds. If Jupiter had more mass, gravity would cause it to shrink and be smaller and denser. Jupiter is as large in diameter as possible for a planet composed of hydrogen and helium.

When I was growing up, Jupiter had 12 known moons, while now there are at least 79! Galileo discovered the four largest moons, and they are called the Galilean moons. After 1975, space probes discovered many smaller moons.

Wikimedia Commons: NASA & ESA A. Simon: public domain

JUPITER ♃

Aphelion	5.459 au
Perihelion	4.950 au
Orbital period	11.862 years
Synodic period	398.88 days
Inclination	1.303°
Diameter	11.209 Earths
Mass	317.8 Earths
Axial tilt	3.13°
Magnitude	-2.94 - -1.66
Angular diam	29.8 – 50.1"
Moons	79

Observing Jupiter

Jupiter is a joy to view in a telescope or binoculars. With binoculars, you can see a disk and the four Galilean moons. With a telescope, you can see the cloud bands that gird the planet. This photograph illustrates how Jupiter and the Galilean moons appear in a telescope. The ability to see detail on Jupiter's disk improves when Jupiter is closer and the disk is larger. Because Jupiter is more distant, the difference in the disk's apparent size at opposition and conjunction is less pronounced than with Mars or Venus. Nevertheless, the ideal observing times are near opposition. Not only is the disk larger, but Jupiter is observable from sunset to sunrise. The table lists opposition dates.

Wikimedia Commons: Jan Sandberg: public domain

Independently, and only months after Galileo, the German astronomer Simon Marius (1573 – 1625) observed the four moons and named them after the lovers of Zeus; Ganymede, Callisto, Io, and Europa, listed here in order of size with the most massive first. Their orbital periods are 7.15, 16.69, 1.77, and 3.55 days, respectively. If it were not for the glare of Jupiter, all four would be visible to the unaided eye. Near opposition, they range in magnitude from 4.6 to 5.7. In a telescope, it's a joy to watch the daily dance around Jupiter as they exchange positions and shift from one side of Jupiter to the other. Occasionally some will pass behind Jupiter and be eclipsed from our view so that you will see fewer than four. When one passes in front of Jupiter, it may cast a shadow on Jupiter's disk.

OPPOSITION	CONST
July 14, 2020	Sagittarius
Aug 19, 2021	Capricornus
Sept 26, 2022	Pisces
Nov 3, 2023	Aries
Dec 7, 2024	Taurus
Jan 10, 2026	Gemini
Feb 10, 2027	Leo
Mar 12, 2028	Leo
Apr 12, 2029	Virgo
May 14, 2030	Libra

The north and south equatorial belts are the easiest to spot in a telescope. A telescope with a larger aperture reveals additional belts. The regions between the belts are referred to as zones. The red spot is on the south side of the south equatorial belt. To view the red spot requires practice and a telescope with at least a four-inch aperture, preferably more.

Two or three months before the opposition, Jupiter will be shining in the west before sunrise. If you have a telescope with a clock drive, you can set Jupiter in the view while it's still dark. It will track Jupiter as the Sun rises, and after a while, you will be able to see Jupiter in the telescope during daylight. With a go-to telescope, Jupiter, Venus, Mars, and the brightest stars can be observed during the day.

Saturn

Saturn is named for the Roman god of wealth and agriculture. It's the second-largest planet in the solar system. Saturn is best known for its beautiful system of rings. The rings are very thin and start at about 4,000 miles from Saturn and extend outward to about 75,000 miles from the planet, but they are less than 100 feet thick. When viewed edge-on, they disappear. The rings are composed primarily of water ice with a smaller amount of simple carbon compounds, small rocks, and dust.

Saturn's moons Pandora and Prometheus shepherd other moons and help confine the rings to their form. The space probe Voyager 1 discovered Pandora. It's oblong and about 85 miles long. Voyager 1 also

Wikimedia Commons: NASA JPL: public domain

SATURN ♄

Aphelion	10.12 au
Perihelion	9.04 au
Orbital period	29.457 years
Synodic period	378.09 days
Inclination	2.485°
Diameter	9.45 Earths
Mass	95.16 Earths
Axial tilt	26.73°
Magnitude	-0.55 - 1.17
Angular diam	14.5 – 20.1"
Moons	82

discovered Prometheus, which is also oblong and about 83 miles long.

Saturn has 82 named moons with many more up to 1500 feet in diameter. The largest, Titan, is larger than our Moon and the planet Mercury. It's spherical and has a dense atmosphere of nitrogen and organics that give it an orange appearance. Saturn's second-largest moon, Rhea, is also spherical and has a Moon-like appearance. The other primary moons of Saturn are Dione, Tethys, Mimas, Enceladus, and Iapetus. The first eight moons were discovered visually by 1848 using telescopes. By 1980, Earth-based telescopic photography found six more. Space probes and digital photography on massive Earth-based telescopes discovered the remaining moons.

Here are a few tidbits about Saturn. Saturn is the least dense of the planets, even less dense than water. If you could find a large enough sea, Saturn would float. The disk of Saturn appears light brown and relatively featureless. But occasionally, great white spots appear. Another white spot is due. The winds in the atmosphere are even stronger than those on Jupiter. Voyager probes recorded winds of over 1,000 miles per hour. And finally, scientists suggest that diamonds rain deep within Saturn.

Observing Saturn

Because Saturn is farther from Earth, the difference in its apparent size and magnitude changes little as it orbits the Sun. Nevertheless, the best viewing times are around oppositions. Saturn's axial tilt is 26.73°, slightly greater than that of the Earth. Because of this tilt, the rings are presented to us with different tilts during Saturn's orbit around the Sun. Every 13 to 16 years, the rings are edge-on and essentially disappear from view. Sunlight reflecting off Saturn's rings contributes to its visual brightness. At full ring tilt, Saturn is about half a magnitude brighter than when the rings are edge-on. Column two in the table gives the

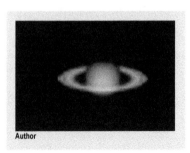
Author

approximate tilt as a percentage of full tilt on various opposition dates. Column three gives the constellation Saturn calls home during opposition.

There are gaps in the rings of Saturn. The most prominent gap is the Cassini division that is barely visible in this image, depicting how Saturn appears in an amateur telescope. Giovanni Cassini (1625 – 1712), an Italian-born mathematician and astronomer who moved to France, discovered this gap in 1675. The Encke gap is another more challenging gap, first observed from Earth in 1888. The Voyager space probes revealed thousands of small gaps in Saturn's rings. These gaps develop from various causes, including

OPPOSITION	TILT	CONST
July 20,2020	70% S	Sagittarius
Aug 2, 2021	55% S	Capricornus
Aug 14, 2022	40% S	Capricornus
Aug 27, 2023	25% S	Aquarius
Sept 8, 2024	10% S	Aquarius
Sept 21, 2025	5% N	Pisces
Oct 4, 2026	20% N	Cetus
Oct 18, 2027	35% N	Pisces
Oct 30, 2028	50% N	Aries
Nov 13, 2029	65% N	Aries
Nov 27, 2030	80% N	Taurus

shepherding by small moons within the gaps and orbital resonances with one or more moons outside the gaps.

Five of Saturn's moons: Titan, Rhea, Dione, Enceladus, and Tethys, are observable with three-inch aperture and larger telescopes. Titan is by far the easiest to observe. It orbits Saturn with a period of 16 days with a maximum separation of about ten times the rings' extent. The closest is Tethys, with a period of 1.9 days and a maximum separation about equal to twice the extent of the rings.

Conjunctions

Because the planets never wander far from the ecliptic and travel through the ecliptic at different rates, a planet may appear to approach another planet or the Moon. These events are referred to as conjunctions. Because the planets are among the brightest objects in the night sky, these conjunctions can be breathtakingly beautiful.

This list of conjunctions includes only the brightest or more interesting conjunctions. The third column, MIN, is the apparent angular separation of the two planets at the closest approach. One minute is 1/60th of a degree. For example, the angular diameter of the Moon as viewed from Earth ranges from 29 to 34 minutes, or about ½ a degree. The separation may be slightly greater at the time of viewing at your location. The last column is the time the event may be seen. Evening refers to viewing after sunset, and morning refers to viewing before sunrise.

DATE	PLANETS	MIN	NOTE
Dec 21, 2020	Jupiter/Saturn	6.1	Eve
Feb 11, 2021	Venus/Jupiter	25.8	Morn
Mar 5, 2021	Mercury/Jupiter	19.5	Morn
May 28, 2021	Mercury/Venus	24.1	Eve
April 30, 2022	Venus/Jupiter	13.8	Morn
Mar 2, 2023	Venus/Jupiter	29.3	Eve
Jan 27, 2024	Mercury/Mars	14.6	Morn
Jun 4, 2024	Mercury/Jupiter	6.8	Morn
Aug 14, 2024	Mars/Jupiter	18.4	Morn
Aug 12, 2025	Venus/Jupiter	51.6	Morn
Apr 20, 2026	Mercury/Saturn	27.6	Morn
Aug 15, 2026	Mercury/Jupiter	33.1	Morn
May 7, 2027	Venus/Saturn	36.3	Morn
Aug 25, 2027	Venus/Jupiter	29.7	Eve
Nov 24, 2027	Venus/Mars	18.6	Eve
Jan 8, 2028	Mercury/Mars	40.7	Eve
Oct 22, 2028	Mercury/Jupiter	57.2	Morn
Nov 9, 2028	Venus/Jupiter	36.7	Morn

The Christmas story in Matthew of the King James Version includes "...there came wise men from the east...for we have seen his star in the east, and we are come to worship him ...and lo, the star, which they saw in the east, went before them, till it stood over where the young child was." Numerous authors have attempted to link the Christmas Star to celestial events.

A popular candidate for the Star of the East is the conjunction of planets. Rarely they may appear so close that the eyes perceive them as a single object. They would look like a single bright star. One translation of Magi is astrologer or astronomer, and if so, they would have noticed the approaching planets and been able to predict the event in advance. In those days, conjunctions were viewed as signaling great events, and there were several conjunctions about that time. Jupiter and Saturn were in conjunction in 7 BC. Jupiter, associated with righteousness in Roman culture, and Regulus, meaning "little king," were in conjunction in 3 BC. Jupiter was in conjunction with Venus, the planet of love and fertility, in June of 2 BC. Because of retrograde motion, Jupiter appeared to stop wandering in December of 2 BC. These are undoubtedly interesting circumstances. Of course, another explanation for the Star of Bethlehem is that it was a divine miracle heralding the birth of Jesus.

Uranus

The seventh planet from the Sun, Uranus, is named after the Greek god, who was the father of Saturn and the grandfather of Jupiter. The diameter of Uranus is four times that of Earth, and it's 14.5 times more massive. Uranus takes just over 84 years to complete an orbit of the Sun. Uranus has 27 moons, named after Shakespeare characters. The largest two moons, Oberon and Titania, are the king and queen of the fairies in *A Midsummer Night's Dream*. They were discovered by Herschel six years after he discovered Uranus in 1781. Uranus is unusual in that its rotational axis is tilted sideways and almost parallel to its orbital plane.

Jupiter and Saturn are referred to collectively as the gas giants. The atmospheric composition of Uranus is primarily hydrogen and

Wikimedia Commons: NASA: public domain

URANUS ♅

Aphelion	20.11 au
Perihelion	18.33 au
Orbital period	84.02 years
Synodic period	369.66 days
Inclination	0.773°
Diameter	4.01 Earths
Mass	14.54 Earths
Axial tilt	97.77°
Magnitude	5.38 – 6.03
Angular diam	3.3 – 4.1"
Moons	27

helium, like Jupiter and Saturn. But because Uranus and the next planet Neptune are further from the Sun and colder, they are referred to as the ice giants.

DATE	OBJECT	MIN	NOTE
Apr 20, 2024	Jupiter	30.5	Eve
July 15, 2024	Mars	32.1	Morn
Apr 23, 2026	Venus	45.2	Eve
July 4, 2026	Mars	6.3	Morn
June 23, 2028	Mars	11.6	Morn

At magnitude 5.4 to 6, Uranus is at the limit of naked-eye visibility. Viewing it requires dark skies and knowing where to look. Uranus is easy to see in binoculars, and the best way to find it is to wait for conjunction with an easily found object like a bright planet. Listed here are favorable conjunctions in the decade of the 2020s. Uranus has a noticeably green appearance and will show a disk in a larger telescope.

Neptune

Wikimedia Commons: NASA Voyager 2 J. Cowart: public domain

NEPTUNE ♆

Aphelion	30.33 au
Perihelion	29.81 au
Orbital period	164.8 years
Synodic period	367.49 days
Inclination	1.768°
Diameter	3.883 Earths
Mass	17.15 Earths
Axial tilt	28.32°
Magnitude	7.67- 8.00
Angular diam	2.2 – 2.4"
Moons	14

The farthest planet from the Sun is Neptune, named for the Roman god of the sea. Although slightly more massive than its ice-giant-twin Uranus, Neptune is of smaller diameter because the higher mass compresses its atmosphere.

Earlier, I wrote that early planetary motion calculations didn't include the planets' gravitational effects on each other. Because the Sun is by far the most massive body in the solar system, the error is small. Nevertheless, unexplained deviations in Uranus' expected position lead two astronomers to independently predict a new planet's position. The French astronomer and mathematician Urbain Le Verrier (1811- 1877) sent his calculations to the Berlin Observatory where Johann Galle (1812 – 1910) discovered Neptune within 1° of the predicted position on September 23, 1846. Another French astronomer wrote Le Verrier discovered a planet *"with the point of a pen."*

Interestingly, Neptune had been observed by Galileo and by other astronomers, who recognized it only as a star. Because of its distance from the Sun, Neptune wanders very slowly among the stars. It requires an excellent telescope to resolve a disk and therefore looks much like a star. It's too dim to see with the naked eye. However, it's easily found with an amateur go-to telescope.

Neptune has 14 moons. The largest, Triton, was discovered 17 days after Neptune. It orbits in retrograde, the opposite direction of Neptune's rotation, so it was probably captured rather than forming with the planet. The moon Neso orbits farther from its host than any other known moon in the solar system. It orbits farther from Neptune than the planet Mercury from the Sun.

The Sun, the eight planets, and asteroids are not the only bodies in the solar system. The solar system includes so many other objects that they almost defy classification. This leads to the story of poor Pluto, once a proud planet that lost its title.

Pluto

Clyde Tombaugh discovered Pluto in 1930. It was named for the Greek underworld god and given the status of the ninth planet. Lowell Observatory received over a thousand suggestions for a name. The name Pluto was suggested by Venetia Burney, an eleven-year-old schoolgirl in Oxford, England, who was interested in mythology.

It takes Pluto almost 248 years to complete an orbit around the Sun. It's the ninth-largest diameter body orbiting the Sun but the tenth most massive. Ironically at perihelion, it's inside the orbit of Neptune. Pluto's potential collision with Neptune is avoided by an orbital resonance between the two bodies.

Further observations of the orbit of Uranus lead astronomers in the late 19th century to speculate on a ninth planet. The founder of Lowell Observatory, and believer in

Wikimedia Commons: NASA: public domain

PLUTO ♇

Aphelion	49.305 au
Perihelion	29.658 au
Orbital period	247.94 yrs
Synodic period	366.73 days
Inclination	17.16°
Diameter	0.1868 Earths
Mass	0.0022 Earths
Axial tilt	122.53°
Magnitude	13.6- 16.3
Angular diam	0.06 – 0.11"
Moons	5

Martian canals, Percival Lowell, had initiated a search in 1906. He died in 1916, and the observatory director reinitiated a search using a new observer, Clyde Tombaugh. He compared multiple photographs taken on three nights to discover Pluto. He took confirming photographs, and the news was announced on March 13, 1930. It turns out Lowell had photographed Pluto before his death but hadn't identified it as a planet.

NASA's New Horizons spacecraft, the only space probe to pass by Pluto, took this image in 2015. In 1992, a Jet Propulsion Lab (JPL) scientist asked Tombaugh for permission to visit the planet. Tombaugh remembered telling him *"he was welcome to it."* One ounce of Clyde Tombaugh's ashes is onboard New Horizons.

Pluto has five known moons. The largest, Charon, was photographed in 1965 but thought to be a photographic defect. Later research in 1978 by astronomer James Christy at the US Naval Observatory revealed it to be a moon. New Horizons took detailed images of Charon and pictures of the other four moons.

Pluto's planetary status declined over time. The original estimate in 1931 of Pluto's mass was similar to Earth. A later estimate was close to the mass of Mars. When Charon was discovered in 1978, its orbit around Pluto provided a more accurate estimate of the mass at 0.2% of Earth's. The nail in the coffin came in 2005 when the solar system body Eris and its moon Dysnomia were discovered. Although slightly smaller in diameter, Eris is more massive than Pluto. The choice was to name Eris the tenth planet or to call Pluto something else. Other bodies in the area of Pluto's orbit were discovered.

In 2006, the IAU resolved to call Pluto and Eris minor planets. The resolution naturally met with scorn. By 2008, the IAU attempted appeasement by calling objects similar to Pluto as plutoids. So, as it stands, Pluto classifications include dwarf planet, minor planet, trans-Neptunian object, plutoid, Kuiper Belt object, kuiperoids, and mesoplanet. Why couldn't they just have named Eris the tenth planet and called it Goofy? The minor planets could then have been called Mini planets. Eris is named for the Greek goddess of discord and strife. How appropriate!

Kuiper Belt and Oort Cloud

The Kuiper Belt is a large group of small bodies extending from Neptune at 30 au from the Sun out to about 50 au. Pluto, Eris, and other round bodies of smaller mass are in this belt. Its total mass is several times that of the asteroid belt, and it contains primarily icy bodies rather than the rocky bodies of the asteroid belt. Over 100,000 bodies greater than 62 miles in diameter probably reside in the belt. Most of the Kuiper Belt mass is a disk, much like the asteroid belt.

Even further beyond the Sun than the Kuiper Belt is a theorized Oort Cloud of icy bodies, a remnant of the early solar system formation. The Oort Cloud may consist of an inner disk-like belt and a more-distant scattered halo of objects in a sphere surrounding the solar system. It's believed that comets are dislodged from the Oort Cloud by the gravitational effects of our Milky Way galaxy and passing stars. Some of these dislodged objects fall toward the Sun in highly elliptical orbits and become comets. These Kuiper Belt and Oort Cloud objects don't treat our eyes until they approach the Sun. The best of these comets put on lovely shows.

Comets

Comets originate in either the Kuiper Belt or the Oort Cloud. Comets are composed of water-ice, ices of other hydrocarbons, dust, and rock. The Harvard and Smithsonian astronomer Fred Whipple (1906 – 2004) coined the term dirty snowball to describe the makeup of comets. More recent data suggest they may contain less ice than once thought, suggesting the term icy dirtballs.

Comets become visible as they approach the Sun, and

the heat converts ices into gases. The gas and released dust are blown away from the comet by the solar wind. At this point, the comet has a nucleus, a round coma of released gases, and a tail extending away from the Sun. Spectacular comets may have comas that are much larger than the Earth and tails that are an astronomical unit long. In this comet Hale-Bopp photo, the brighter yellow portion of the tail is sunlight reflecting off dust in the tail, and the bluer, very dim portion above the tail is from gas.

Wikimedia Commons: P. Salzgeber: CC 2.0

Short-period comets with orbital periods under 200 years often have highly elliptical orbits near the ecliptic, orbiting in the same direction as the planets, with aphelion beyond Jupiter. They probably originate from the Kuiper Belt. The famous Comet Halley, which returns every 76 years, is an example of this class. There are almost 400 listed and numbered short-period comets with periods as short as three years. They are typically not bright comets as their frequent visits into the inner solar system have depleted them of their icy component. This image of comet 67P/Churyumov-Gerasimenko is a montage of images acquired by the ESA spacecraft Rosetta in 2014 at a distance of 17.8 miles from the comet. Rosetta entered an orbit with 67P, and the lander Philae made the first-ever landing on a comet. The period of 67P is 6.45 years.

Wikimedia Commons: ESA Rosetta: CC 3.0

Long-period comets have orbital periods over 200 years to millions of years and are often more inclined to the ecliptic. The beautiful Comet West of 1976, with a period of roughly a million years, is a member of this class. Some are one-pass comets with parabolic or hyperbolic orbits. Because comets pass by the outer giant planets, their orbits are sometimes deflected, making the orbits unstable and challenging to predict. Even regular visitors like Halley, recorded as far back as 240 BC, someday may not return.

Comets visible in telescopes are regular visitors, and a few are seen each year. Comets just at naked-eye visibility in dark skies typically happen once a year. Brighter comets are called great comets and happen about once a decade. The best source for knowing where and when to look is astronomy magazines, local newscasts, and local newspapers. The great comets sell telescopes, but the best tool for observing comets is binoculars.

COMET	YEAR	PERIOD
Ikeya-Seki	1965	1000 yr
Bennet	1970	1680 yr
Kohoutek	1973	75,000 yr
West	1976	0.3 to 6 Myr
Halley	1986	75.5 yr
Hyakutake	1996	70,000 yr
Hale-Bopp	1997	2,388 yr
McNaught	2007	93,000? yr
Lovejoy	2011	24,000 yr

Voyager

Many books have covered the exploration of the solar system by space probes. Space probes from ten countries have at least flown by bodies in the solar system. Probes have landed on or into the atmospheres of the Moon, Mercury, Venus, Mars, Jupiter, Saturn, the Saturn moon Titan, asteroids, and comets. I'll mention just two early probes that have left the solar system.

Voyager 2 launched on August 20, 1977, and Voyager 1 was launched sixteen days later, on September 5, 1977. Both Voyager spacecraft included three 157-watt radioisotope thermoelectric generators (RTGs). The radioactive decay of plutonium oxide generates heat used to produce electricity. The RTGs provide enough electricity to operate the Voyagers for 48 years. They are traveling far beyond the Sun, where solar power is minuscule.

The Voyager missions were the exploration of the outer planets. Voyager 1 overtook the previously launched Voyager 2 on December 19, 1977. Voyager 1 visited Jupiter and Saturn, and then Saturn's moon Titan. The visit to Titan took Voyager 1 out of the ecliptic plane and ended its planetary missions.

After passing Saturn, Voyager 2 continued to the planets Uranus and Neptune. The Voyager spacecraft explored the planets and their moons at all wavelengths of the electromagnetic spectrum, visible light, and magnetic fields. The images were stunning, and the science was revealing.

Both spacecraft are now outbound from the Sun. In August of 2012, Voyager 1 passed beyond the Sun's influence and entered interstellar space, followed by Voyager 2 in November of 2018. JPL maintains contact with both probes that continue to gather data about interstellar space and continue to do so as long as the RTGs continue to provide sufficient power.

Onboard the Voyager spacecraft is a gold-plated audio-visual disk with sounds and images of Earth. Provided it's not intercepted by interstellar pirates, in 42,000 years, it will pass by the star Ross 248 but at a distance of 1.7 ly. Next, we will also venture beyond our solar system.

6 Stars

Early astronomers suspected the stars are distant suns. By the 17ᵗʰ century, most astronomers reached this consensus. The study of the Sun served as an essential bridge to understanding the distant stars. The first mystery to solve was the source of the tremendous energy output of the Sun.

The Fuel of Stars

When directly overhead on a clear day, the Sun delivers about 1,000 watts of power to every square meter of ground. That's an easy measurement for scientists to make. The energy is reduced slightly by absorption and reflection of the atmosphere, but let's ignore that. Suppose the Sun is irradiating one square meter with that power. Then it's irradiating every square meter onto the surface of an imaginary sphere with a radius equal to our distance from the Sun. So, if we multiply 1,000 watts by the area of that immense sphere, we have the total output power of the Sun at any moment. It's 3.8×10^{26} watts. The average power production of all fossil fuel, nuclear, wind, hydroelectric, and solar plants in the world is 2.3×10^{12} watts. The Sun produces over 10^{14}, or 100,000,000,000,000 times as much power. Scientists realized early that the Sun wasn't simply burning coal.

Popular explanations in the 1850s were that meteors falling into the Sun or the continual gravitational collapse of the Sun released the energy. Lord Kelvin, of thermodynamics fame, considered both. He calculated an upper limit on the age of the Sun of 30,000,000 years based on the energy available from the collapse of the Sun's mass. Lord Kelvin and Charles Darwin got in a tiff over this because Darwin had estimated the Earth was 10x older than that by working backward from erosion of the Weald valley in England.

SIR ARTHUR EDDINGTON
(1882 - 1944) British physicist,
astronomer, and mathematician

The physicists Röntgen, Curie, and Rutherford's work on radioactivity hinted at a new energy form. But studies of the Sun revealed it contained few radioactive elements and was primarily hydrogen and helium. The next clue came in 1905 with Einstein's famous equation linking mass and energy: $E=mc^2$. It meant that mass multiplied by an enormous number (the velocity of light) squared yielded a lot of energy. In 1920, the brilliant English astronomer, physicist, and mathematician Sir Arthur Eddington (1882 – 1944) proposed that fusion of hydrogen into helium accounted for the Sun's energy.

He was essentially correct. However, the nuclear processes within stars are more complex than just hydrogen fusing into helium. In the extreme temperature of stellar cores, other fusion processes occur as well. As nuclear physics matured, a new discipline combining physics and astronomy was born. Astrophysics became a powerful tool for understanding the Heavens in greater detail.

Stellar Nurseries

Earlier I wrote about the formation of our Sun and the solar system. Most stars do not form individually but in groups, in large hydrogen and helium concentrations scattered throughout their host galaxy. Our Sun probably formed with nearby companions, and scientists are searching for past companion candidates. Our Milky Way galaxy is estimated to hold 6,000 vast regions of gas concentrations that are in the process of forming stars, regions referred to as stellar nurseries or star-forming regions. This Hubble Space Telescope image is the galaxy M83 in the southern constellation Hydra. This galaxy is unusually active in the birthing of stars. The numerous red concentrations are star-forming regions.

A perturbational event often triggers the gravitational collapse that forms stars. Such events might include colliding clouds, a nearby stellar explosion, or the collision (or nearly so) of entire galaxies.

Wikimedia Commons: NASA: public domain

The formation of a huge star that quickly burns through its stash of fuel and explodes can begin forming other stars in its neighborhood.

Stars born within the molecular cloud can excite the gas in the cloud to luminescence. H II regions abound in our Milky Way and images of other galaxies. H is the symbol for hydrogen, and II is the Roman numeral two, signifying that the hydrogen is singly ionized. These regions are pronounced "H two" regions. They produce a red glow at 646 nanometers wavelength. Images of some galaxies show many prominent H II regions.

The Great Orion Nebula

One such H II region in our galaxy is the Great Orion Nebula pictured in this Hubble telescope image. The Orion Nebula's total mass is about 2,000 solar masses, and it's 24 ly across and 1,344 ly from us. Approximately 700 stars are in various forms of development within the nebula, believed to be only a few million years old. Within a million years or so, the young stars' stellar wind will blow the

Wikimedia Commons: NASA: public domain

remaining gas away, and an open cluster of stars minus the nebula will remain. Open star clusters are another common feature of our Milky Way and other galaxies.

Acute eyesight can detect the Great Orion Nebula without optical aid. Given in the chapter Constellations is a chart of the Orion constellation. Orion's sword hangs from the lower left of his belt. Careful observation of the sword reveals that the middle of three stars does not appear quite like a point of light but is instead a blurry object. Binoculars easily show the middle of the sword is not a star but a nebula. Binoculars also show the top and bottom stars of the sword are multiple stars.

Wikimedia Commons: skatebiker: public domain

A small telescope reveals four stars in the center of the brightest part of the nebula. These four stars spaced in the shape of a trapezoid are called the Trapezium. Shown here is how the Great Orion Nebula appears in binoculars. Binoculars and small telescopes show only a little color in the nebula. Large telescopes or long-time exposures are required to reveal brilliant colors.

Proper Motion

The ancients thought stars resided on the furthest celestial sphere, with the planets and Sun on closer spheres. The outer-most sphere of stars was solid and unchanging. This seems natural. As the planets wander among the stars, the stars' arrangement or constellation remains unchanging. But do they?

The English polymath
Edmund Halley (1656 –
1742) discovered that
Halley's comet was a
returning comet. In 1718, he
reported that the positions of
the stars Sirius, Arcturus,
and Aldebaran were more
than half a degree from the
positions recorded by
Hipparchus some 1850 years

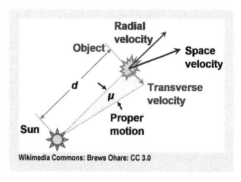

Wikimedia Commons: Brews Ohare: CC 3.0

earlier. That motion is slow and imperceptible to the eyes
during a lifetime. But longer time frames tell a different
story. In the distant past and distant future, the
appearance of the constellations is different.

Of course, the stars are not on the surface of a sphere;
they are placed randomly in space, both in the distance and
direction from us. They are also in constant motion. The
motion has two components: radial velocity directed
toward or away from us and transverse velocity at right
angles to our viewpoint. The radial motion doesn't change
the shape of the constellations. It's measured by observing
the Doppler frequency shift of lines in the star's spectrum.
Transverse motion, called proper motion, results in an
angular shift in the star's position. Over eons, proper
motion changes the shape of the constellations.

Astronomers began recording the radial velocity and
proper motion of stars in the 18th century. The ESA satellite
Hipparcos, launched in 1989, automated the accurate
measurement of the proper motion of over 100,000 stars
and less accurately for over a million. The ESA Gaia
spacecraft launched in 2013, whose mission is to measure a
billion stars' motions, replaced Hipparcos.

The star with the highest proper motion is Barnard's
star, first measured in 1916 by the American astronomer
E.E. Barnard (1857 – 1923), who has a long list of
impressive astronomy achievements. Barnard's star has a
proper motion of 10.3 arcseconds per year. Over Bernard's
lifetime, his star moved almost 2/10 of a degree. This
motion would be discernable by the naked eye were it not

for the fact that Barnard's star at magnitude 9.5 is much too dim to see without optical aid.

Because of its radial velocity, in 10,000 years, Barnard's star will be closer to us than the current closest star is now. But Proxima Centauri is also approaching, and at that time, it will remain the closest star. In 33,000 years, the closest star to us will be Ross 248.

Star Classification

The birth mechanism for all stars is essentially the same. However, not all stars are alike. It's not the composition of the cloud from which the star formed that defines the outcome. It's the total mass involved in the initial gravitational collapse.

The quantitative classification of stars began with the spectroscopic observation of stars in the 1860s. By 1890, the Harvard College Observatory had classified stellar spectrums with consecutive letters A through P, with Q used for unusual stars. As astronomers understood spectrum complexities better, classifications became nonconsecutive. The table lists the current star classification, surface temperature, and star color.

CLASS	TEMP(°K)	COLOR	FRAC
O	>30,000	blue	few
B	10,000-30,000	blue white	0.13%
A	7,500-10,000	white	0.6%
F	6,000-7,500	yellow white	3%
G	5,200-6,000	yellow	7.6%
K	3,700-5,200	light orange	12.1%
M	2.400-3,700	orange red	76.4%

The Sun is a G-class star of moderate size and temperature. G-class stars have a mass of 0.8 to 1.04 solar masses and a radius of 0.96 to 1.15 solar radii. The fraction (FRAC) column is the percentage of known stars in mid-life in each classification.

By the 1920s, a more revealing stellar classification came into use. As the distance to the various stars was determined, their absolute luminosity became known. Around 1910, Ejnar Hertzsprung (1873 – 1967), a Danish astronomer, and Henry Russel (1877 – 1957), an American astronomer, independently plotted absolute stellar luminosity versus the temperature of stars. The format has evolved, but it's still referred to as the Hertzsprung-Russel

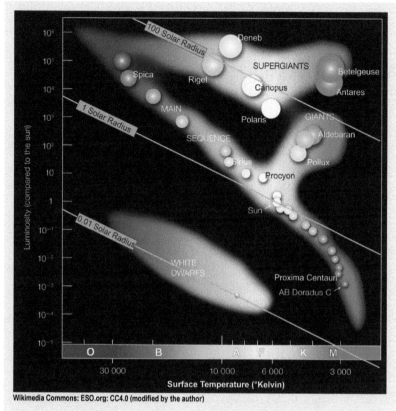

diagram. The diagram became a revealing tool for understanding stellar evolution.

Stars enter life somewhere on the Main Sequence, extending from the lower right to the upper left. Low-mass stars begin life as low-temperature red stars on the lower right of the diagram. Mid-mass stars like the Sun begin life near the middle of the Main Sequence. Massive stars begin life near the upper right. The lower temperature in the core of low-mass stars fuses hydrogen very slowly. They can live longer than the current age of the universe. Moderate-mass stars like the Sun have a lifetime of about ten billion years. Stars like Spica with a mass of over ten Suns may live only ten million years. Because lower-mass stars have a longer lifetime, the quantity of existing stars in a given class tends to increase with lower mass.

The gray diagonal lines delineate the radius of stars relative to the Sun. The tiniest stars have a radius of about

1/10 the Sun's, and the radius of the largest stars on the main sequence is about ten times the Sun's.

Stellar Population

In 1944, a German-born astronomer working at Mt. Wilson Observatory, Walter Baade (1893 – 1960), divided stars into two groups. Population I stars are younger and have higher metallicity as determined by their spectrum. Astronomy defines elements with an atomic weight greater than helium as metals, including carbon, oxygen, and all the other heavier elements. This definition is different than that for solid metals that conduct electricity. Astronomy uses this term as a shortcut for "all elements other than hydrogen or helium."

The distinction is important because the early universe contained hydrogen and helium primarily. Older Population II stars fused these elements into heavier elements and enriched the interstellar medium with the heavier elements. Younger Population I stars, like our Sun, formed in this later universe and are richer in metals. Population II stars contain hydrogen and helium primarily and are metal-poor.

Baade discovered the Milky Way arms are predominantly young Population I stars and tend to be bluer than the older and more yellow Population II stars in the galactic core. Later, I'll write about the globular clusters of stars that surround the Milky Way. They are not confined just to the disk. Globular clusters are ancient and are composed of Population II stars.

Star Names and Catalogs

The IAU currently recognizes proper names for over 300 stars, but the list is growing. Many proper names are Arabic versions of names in Ptolemy's *Almagest*. They often refer to the star's position within its parent constellation, such as Rigel, Arabic for the foot of Orion. Other stars bear original Greek or Latin names such as Sirius for "scorching." Other names have a modern derivation, such as Regor, Roger spelled backward after astronaut Roger Chaffee who died in the Apollo I pad fire.

Throughout this book, I'll use the Bayer designation for stars first proposed by the German Johann Bayer (1572 – 1625) in 1603. Sequential letters of the Greek alphabet followed by the constellation name identify stars. For example, α Orion is the Bayer identification for Betelgeuse. The dimmest Bayer identified star in Orion is then ω Orion. Bayer originally listed 1,564 stars in his catalog.

The Flamsteed system established in 1783 uses numbers rather than Greek letters followed by the constellation name. In this case, the numbers increase sequentially based on position within the constellation from west to east. In the 1880s, Harvard College Observatory began taking spectrums and cataloging stars in a program initially funded by amateur astronomer Henry Draper's widow. By 2017, that program had cataloged over 359,000 stars. Each star has a catalog number beginning with HD. The Draper catalog remains popular.

Once automated telescopes began cataloging stars, the numbers rapidly increased. The Hubble Guide Star Catalog II, published in 2008, has magnitudes, classifications, and positions of 455,851,237 stars.

Multiple Star Systems

Remember that iconic scene in the original Star Wars film? It's one of the more poignant in cinema. Luke Skywalker is staring at the twin sunset of Tatooine while he ponders his future. It turns out twin suns are common. The majority of stars are members of multiple star systems. Two gravitationally bound stars are called binaries, or double stars. Triples may be even more common than binaries, and higher-order systems exist. Associations are sometimes circumstantial. For example, Beta Cephi consists of a real binary and a third star in a similar sightline that is not at the same distance and not gravitationally bound to the binary.

The orbits of multiple star systems may or may not be stable. A pair of stars in close orbit with a more distant third star orbiting the binary can form a stable system. Quadruple systems with two sets of binaries are relatively common. The orbits of three or more stars at similar distances from each other may be chaotic and eventually eject a member. The dynamics of a large number of stars are complex. Systems with a large number of stars are designated as clusters rather than multiple star systems.

Observing Multiples

There are thousands of multiple star systems within the range of small telescopes, but no two are alike. The color of each star, each star's magnitude, and the separation of the stars make each system unique, and what makes observing them interesting. The table lists a few representative multiples to observe.

The first and second columns are the constellation and name of the star system. The chapter Constellations provides instructions and charts for finding the listed constellations. The third column in the list is the magnitude of the individual stars in the system.

The fourth column is the visual separation of the stars in seconds of arc. PA is an abbreviation for the position angle of the dimmer star from the brighter star. When observing, imagine a line from the brighter star to the dimmer star. If that line points north, the PA is 0°. If the line is east, the PA is 90°, south is 180°, etc.

When observing, the ability to see that the system is two stars is resolving or splitting the double. Brighter stars

CONST	STAR	MAGS	SEP(")	PA(°)	OPTICS
Ursa Major	Alcor, Mizar	2.2, 4.0	708	205	Eye
Gemini	65 & 64	5.0, 5.1	818	333	Eye
Scorpius	μ	3.1, 3.6	347	72	Eye
Taurus	θ	3.4, 3.9	337	347	Eye
Cygnus	β	3.2, 4.7	35	55	Bino
Cygnus	o	3.9, 7, 4.8	109, 337	173, 322	Bino
Cygnus	Alberio	3.1 – 5.1	35	55	Bino
Draco	υ	4.9, 4.9	62	311	Bino
Orion	Trapesium	5.1 – 7.5	8.9-21.4	Multiple	Tele
Lyra	Double-Double	5.2 – 6.1	2.3 - 209	Multiple	Tele

of similar magnitude are easier to split, and of course, stars with greater separation are easier to split.

A good test of eyesight is the naked eye double Alcor and Mizar, the middle stars of the handle of Ursa Major, the Big Dipper. My granddaughter can split them, but I can't. Actually, Alcor is a double, and Mizar is a quadruple system. A small telescope doesn't resolve the Alcor double, and Mizar resolves into two stars. Gemini 65 & 64 are also naked eye doubles in very dark skies. Scorpius μ and Taurus θ are also naked eye doubles in dark skies for persons with keen eyesight.

While naked eye splitting of doubles is a fun challenge, multiple star systems can be Heavenly with optical aid. Cygnus β, Cygnus o, Alberio, and Draco υ are examples of binocular doubles. Alberio is a stunning double because the brighter star is orange, and the dimmer star is blue.

One of the more famous quadruple star systems is the telescopic Trapezium in the Great Orion Nebula's brightest portion. Another fun quadruple system in the Lyra ε, the Double-Double. In binoculars, this star appears to be a double. With a larger amateur telescope, each double star appears as a close double. The position angles of the close doubles are at a right angle to each other. It's a remarkable sight.

Eclipsing Binaries

When the Earth's position aligns with the orbital plane of binary stars, one star eclipses the other, called eclipsing binaries. Unless the two stars are close, or one is much larger than the other, the alignment must be precise, and therefore the likelihood any two binaries will eclipse is slim. Nevertheless, because of the large number of multiple star systems, thousands of eclipsing binaries are cataloged.

The most famous of eclipsing binaries is Algol, the second brightest star in the constellation Perseus. Actually,

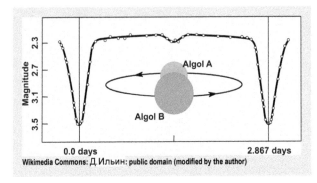

Wikimedia Commons: Д.Ильин: public domain (modified by the author)

Algol is a triple-star system. The third star is further from the eclipsing pair and doesn't eclipse.

Algol A is more massive and luminous than Algol B, but Algol B is larger in diameter. When Algol B partially eclipses Algol A, the total magnitude visually drops from 2.3 to 3.5, as shown in the light curve's dips on the right and left. When the brighter Algol A passes in front of Algol B, there is a minor dip in magnitude. The period between dips is 2.867 days. The dip is quite noticeable and is fun to observe by comparing the brightness of Algol to nearby stars. Algol may be found using the star chart for the constellation Perseus in the chapter on constellations. The website *skyandtelescope.org/observing/celestial-objects-to-watch/the-minima-of-algol/* may be used to find times for the magnitude minimum.

Variable Stars

We are lucky that our star is stable. The Sun's gradual warming since the Maunder minimum in the 1700s is slight, although that period is also referred to as the little ice age in Europe. Satellite measurement of the total solar irradiance above our atmosphere has a history of only four decades. That data suggests a relationship between solar irradiance and sunspot activity. Astrophysical models of the Sun predict the Sun will slowly warm over the next few billion years, and eventually, the Sun will swell until its photosphere swallows the Earth. But for now, the Sun rises every morning and bathes us in a reasonably constant glow.

Not all stars are so well-behaved. Eclipsing binaries are extrinsically variable stars. The stars themselves are stable, but the eclipsing blocks some of the light. However, the output of intrinsic variables is due to the dynamic instability of the star. The brightness of some stars varies by a factor of thousands, while some vary only slightly. The variability period may be irregular or regular, and periods vary from hours to years. There are scores of classification of variable star types.

This shortlist represents a few types of variable stars. The star γ Cass, the middle star in the W of Cassiopeia, is an eruptive variable, with that variable class given that star's name. In the late 1930s, it had what is called a shell episode, brightened to about 1.6, and then dropped rapidly to 3.4. It has since brightened back to about magnitude 2.2. The star χ Cygnus is a Mira class variable that pulsates regularly with a period greater than 100 days. They are red giant stars in the late stage of life. This star varies from an easily seen star in dark skies to invisibility with a period of just over a year. β Lyra is another eclipsing binary like Algol.

STAR	MAG min	MAG max	PERIOD(days)	TYPE
γ Cass	2	3.4		Gamma Cassiopeia
χ Cygn	3.3	14.2	408	Mira
β Lyra	3.25	4.36	12.914	Eclipsing Binary
RS Ophi	4.3	12.5		Recurrent nova
α Orio	0	1.7	2334	Semiregular
α Umin	1.86	2.13	3.97	Classical Cepheid

RS Ophiuchus is a recurrent nova that has erupted eight times since 1898, the last being in 2006. It's a red giant with a white dwarf companion. The white dwarf steals gas from the giant, which eventually causes a thermonuclear burst on the dwarf. α Orion is the red-giant Betelgeuse, the largest star visible to the naked eye, larger than the orbit of Mars. It's currently the second brightest star in Orion. It has the Bayer designation α because it was once brighter than Rigel. Beginning in October of 2019, it began dimming from magnitude 0.5 to 1.7 within a few months. Betelgeuse is near the end of its life and will supernova probably within 100,000 years.

Perhaps the most famous and vital class of variable stars is pulsating Cepheids. There are various subclasses of the Cepheids, but they share one important property. The period of their variability depends directly on their absolute luminosity. More luminous Cepheids have longer periods. The importance of this will be evident when I later write about the expansion of the universe. Polaris, the North Star, listed as α Ursa Minor, is a Cepheid variable.

The Bright Stars

Listed in the table are stars brighter than the first magnitude. Because these stars are brighter than neighboring stars, they are easy to find using star charts. They each have their own color, brightness, season, and place in the sky. With a bit of practice, they become recognizable at a glance. Alpha Centauri, Achernar, Hadar, and Acrux are in the southern celestial hemisphere and are not visible from the United States.

The brightest star, Sirius the scorcher, is in Canis Major, the faithful dog that follows the great hunter Orion as he wanders westward on Winter evenings. Canopus, the second brightest star, shines just above the southern horizon for viewers in the deep south. Its low altitude above the horizon dims the star and turns the bluish color more yellow. It's a beautiful sight for observers in the

RANK	MAG	NAME	CONST	DIST(ly)	COLOR
1	−1.46	Sirius	Canis Major	8.6	Silver Blue
2	−0.74	Canopus	Carina	310	Silver Blue
3	−0.27	Alpha Centauri	Centaurus	4.4	Yellow
4	−0.05	Arcturus	Bootes	37	Red
5	0.03 (-0.02 to 0.07)	Vega	Lyra	25	Silver Blue
6	0.08 (0.03 to 0.16)	Capella	Auriga	43	Yellow
7	0.13 (0.05 to 0.18)	Rigel	Orion	860	Blue
8	0.34	Procyon	Canis Minor	11	White
9	0.46 (0.40 to 0.46)	Achernar	Eridanus	139	Blue
10	0.50 (0.2 to 1.2)	Betelgeuse	Orion	700	Deep Red
11	0.61	Hadar	Centaurus	390	Blue
12	0.76	Altair	Aquila	17	Silver Blue
13	0.76	Acrux	Crux	320	Blue
14	0.86 (0.75 to 0.95)	Aldebaran	Taurus	65	Red
15	0.96 (0.6 to 1.6)	Antares	Scorpius	550	Deep Red
16	0.97 (0.97 to 1.04)	Spica	Virgo	250	Blue

southern US as it peeks above the southern horizon for a brief time each night during the Winter.

As Summer begins, the blue star Spica in the constellation Virgo passes to the south, and soon after that, the bright red star Arcturus in Bootes passes overhead. A couple of hours later, the red star Antares, the heart of Scorpius, rises in the southern sky. Vega, the star featured in the movie Contact, passes overhead next in late Summer, just ahead of the beautiful constellation Cygnus, the Swan. Altair and Vega, along with the star Deneb (just off the list at magnitude 1.25), form the large asterism called the Summer Triangle shining overhead.

Winter is the time to view the bright yellow star Capella in Auriga in the north. Aldebaran in Taurus has just passed overhead, and further south is Betelgeuse and Rigel in Orion. Procyon soon follows about the same height above the southern horizon as Betelgeuse.

For variable stars, the table gives the magnitude range in parenthesis. Variable stars cause inconsistencies in the list. At the time of this writing, Betelgeuse is magnitude 1.3 and would not even be on the list, let alone in 10th place.

Star Death

Once a region of a molecular cloud gravitationally collapses to a sufficient density and temperature, hydrogen fusion begins. The outward pressure of the released energy halts the collapse, and a star is born. Stars that had accumulated small amounts of hydrogen before fusion began are called red dwarfs. The Sun is a moderate-mass star. Stars much more massive than the Sun are bluer and hotter.

Stars begin their life, and for a while, remain on the Main sequence of the H-R diagram for fusing primarily hydrogen. What happens next depends on the star's initial mass. For stars with the Sun's mass and somewhat more massive, as the hydrogen becomes depleted, hydrogen continues to fuse in a shell surrounding an inert helium core. Our Sun will expand and become a red giant. Then, in less than a billion years, the core and shell's nuclear processes evolve through several phases. A massive solar

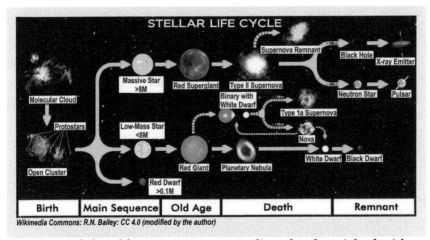

wind then blows away an expanding cloud enriched with oxygen and carbon. The Sun will collapse into a white dwarf whose light excites the expanding cloud into a gloriously visible ring of colors called a planetary nebula. Amateur telescopes reveal planetary nebulae scattered about the heavens. If a red giant accompanies a white dwarf companion, the dwarf can steel gas from the giant, causing a brief but violent explosion of the white dwarf visible as a nova. These explosions can repeat as a recurrent nova or end in an extremely violent supernova.

Novae

Novae suddenly brighten and then decline in magnitude. Different nuclear processes result in multiple novae classes identifiable by their light curves versus time. A decline of two magnitudes typically takes one to three months. Novae may be single events or recurrent. Occasionally novae are close enough to Earth to be relatively bright. Nova Cygni 1975 reached a peak magnitude of 2, as bright as nearby Deneb. Roughly ten novae a year are observed in the Milky Way, but there are probably five times as many annually. The dust and gas clouds of the Milky Way obscure many from our view.

Stars initially larger than eight solar masses eventually form supernovae, producing a visible supernova remnant cloud, and culminating in either a black hole or a pulsar star. In 1572, Tycho Brahe observed a supernova in the constellation Cassiopeia, calling it a "nova stella," Latin for new star, and the term nova stuck.

Supernovae are even more energetic than novae. Supernovae are the final gasp of massive stars that result from a runaway thermonuclear reaction. A single star may outshine an entire galaxy for weeks or months. The most recently recorded supernova in our Milky Way galaxy was Kepler's Supernova of 1604. Astronomers estimate there are about three supernovae per century in the Milky Way. The most recent naked eye supernova was SN 1987A in the Large Magellanic Cloud, a satellite galaxy of the Milky Way visible in the Southern Hemisphere. Supernovae occur regularly in distant galaxies, and amateur astronomers discover many of them.

Neutron Stars and Pulsars

The final state of a supernova type II also depends on the star's initial mass. If the initial star's mass is less than about 30 or 40 solar masses, the supernova's remnant star is a neutron star. The explosion expels most of the material. Fusion stops, and the remaining mass collapses until gravity is so strong the electrons and protons of atoms merge and become neutrons. All that remains is neutrons. The density is that of an atomic nucleus. A neutron star with the mass of the Sun would be only a few miles across.

These neutron stars retain angular momentum from the parent star. As the remnant collapses, the spin becomes rapid, sometimes rotating hundreds of times in a second. Their rotating strong magnetic field produces radiation emanating from the star's poles. If the rotational axis happens to be aligned correctly, we see the radiation flashing like a lighthouse beacon. The radiation frequency spans the entire spectrum from radio waves, through light, to gamma rays. A radio telescope discovered the first pulsar in 1967, resulting in a Nobel Prize for the discoverer. Pulsars had been predicted shortly before the discovery.

Black Holes

Supernovae explosions expel most of the stellar material. For stars initially larger than about 40 solar masses, the remaining neutron star is larger than two solar masses. In this case, gravitational forces are so strong that a collapse continues. Gravity's pull decreases with distance squared. We are attracted to the center of mass of the Earth, but that center is approximately four thousand miles beneath our feet. If the radius of the Earth were only forty miles, I would weigh 1,800,000 pounds. The supernova remnant's collapse becomes so extreme, and the force of gravity so strong that not even light can escape.

How can we know black holes exist if we can't "see" them? We see their influence on objects in their neighborhood. Like any massive object, they have a gravitational effect on objects near them. Astronomers have discovered stars orbiting around a black hole at the center of our Milky Way galaxy. The orbits of these visible stars reveal that this black hole is supermassive with a mass equal to about four million Suns.

When gas clouds or stars get too close to a black hole, they accelerate to speeds near the velocity of light, and they begin emitting radio waves and X-rays. Radio telescopes detected these accretion disk signals before black holes were understood or known to exist.

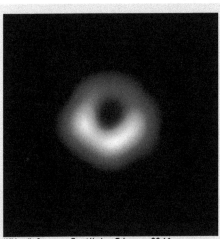

A research team with the Event Horizon Telescope, an international consortium of radio telescopes linked together throughout the globe, created this depiction of an area around an object in the galaxy M87 in the constellation Virgo. This depiction is not a photograph. It's called a false-color image because the image is not of light. It results from a computer algorithm processing vast amounts of radio signal data into a representation of the radio signals' shape. Positioned in space near this black hole, you wouldn't see this image. The dark region in the center is called the shadow of the black hole.

The actual size, if the word "size" is appropriate, of the black hole is a matter of conjecture. Scientists agree that the region's size from which light can't escape is larger than the black hole itself. They also agree that this size depends only on the mass of the black hole. The distance from the black hole center at which light can't escape is called the Schwarzschild radius, named after the German astronomer Karl Schwarzschild (1873 – 1916). He first calculated the radius using Einstein's equations of general relativity. The "surface" of this sphere is called the event horizon.

Black holes don't necessarily wander around swallowing up things. Stable orbits can exist around them. If the Sun were to collapse into a black hole (there is no reason for it to do so), the event horizon would be smaller than the current surface of the Sun, and the planets would continue to orbit around it. It would disappear, light and heat would not escape, and we would freeze.

Star Stuff

The Big Bang theory postulates that soon after the beginning, the universe contained only the lightest elements; hydrogen, helium, and some lithium with one, two, and three protons in the nucleus, respectively. After hundreds of millions of years, the stars began forming out of this soup in a process like our Sun and solar system's formation.

However, the Earth has carbon, oxygen, and even much heavier elements like iron, gold, and uranium. From where did these elements come? The first stars looked and behaved like stars we know today, but they were void of the heavy elements. These stars were busily manufacturing the heavy elements through the process of fusion. As stars ran out of hydrogen, they began fusing some of the slightly heavier elements. The merger of older stars also produced heavier elements. Nova and supernova produced even heavier elements. These violent eruptions scattered heavy elements throughout space, which mixed with the abundant hydrogen and helium that had not yet formed stars.

Later-generation stars with planetary systems that formed out of this mixture contained heavier elements. The Sun is such a system. The Sun formed billions of years after previous stars had cooked up the heavier elements. In the 1980 Public Broadcasting Service TV series *Cosmos: A Personal Voyage*, Carl Sagan famously said, "*It makes some sense to revere the Sun and stars, because, we are their children.*" We are literally made of stardust.

7 The Milky Way

Almost everything in the Heavens that you can see with your unaided eyes resides in our home galaxy, the Milky Way. This local neighborhood is over 150,000 ly across and contains over 100 billion Suns. It's a rotating pinwheel disk with four or five arms or pieces of arms. Our arm is called the Orion arm, and Earth lies about 27,000 ly from the galactic center. It takes us 240 million years to rotate around the galaxy. If you find it difficult to imagine the Earth is spinning 1,000 mph at the equator, imagine we are spinning around the Milky Way at 500,000 mph.

The Milky Way

We see a concentration of very dim and distant stars in the galaxy's disk and call it the Milky Way. We look toward the center of the galaxy in the Summer and the outer arms in the Winter. The individual stars we see are closer stars in our arm of the Milky Way. Amongst his many other discoveries, when he turned his telescope on the Heavens, Galileo first saw that the Milky Way was a vast number of stars. You can repeat the discovery by simply looking at the Milky Way through binoculars.

The exact structure of the Milky Way is uncertain. It's the classic can't see the forest for the trees problem. A careful comparison of data compiled using different methods, and examination of other galaxies, results in a consensus that the Milky Way is a barred spiral similar to this image of galaxy UGC 12158 taken with the HST. The Milky Way certainly includes a central bulge and concentration of stars with a supermassive black hole, a disk of arms containing stellar concentrations, visible dust

143

Wikimedia Commons: ESA & NASA: public domain

lanes in the arms, and an outer halo of globular clusters. Our galaxy is host to many interesting features that tell us the universe's story. Small telescopes and binoculars reveal the story in ways our eyes alone cannot. That is the subject of this chapter.

By the way, the English playwright John Heywood (1497 – 1580) was a treasure trove of epigrams. Besides the "you cannot see the wood for the trees," he gave us "Rome was not built in a day," "this hitteth the nail on the head," "no man ought to look a given horse in the mouth," "better late than never," "haste maketh waste," and others you would recognize.

Charles Messier

Wikimedia Commons: R. Stoyan: public domain
CHARLES MESSIER
(1730 – 1817) French astronomer

Charles Messier (1730 – 1817) was an astronomer for the French Navy. He was also a comet hunter and discovered thirteen comets using a 100 mm (4-inch) refractor. Comets are found by regularly sweeping the skies for dim fuzzy objects which appear when they approach the Sun from the outer regions of the solar system. Until recent decades, most comets were found by amateurs using modest telescopes. Today, automated telescopes searching for objects that threaten the Earth now find most new comets.

When the comet hunter finds a suspected object, they observe the same area of sky on successive nights to verify the object's movement. However, many other permanent celestial objects appear similar to comets. To avoid confusion, Messier and an associate, Pierre Mechain, began cataloging these celestial objects. By 1781 the catalog had grown to 103 objects. In the 20th century, historians discovered the two had observed seven more not in the published catalog, for a total of 110. We identify Messier's objects using the designation M following by the sequential number of the discovery. For example, the Great Orion Nebula is M42. Because modest telescopes and even binoculars reveal these objects, amateurs use the Messier catalog as an interesting list of objects to observe. Professional astronomers also often identify these objects by their Messier catalog number.

In the following sections, as I describe various celestial objects in the Milky Way, Messier objects will be given as examples. Tables of Messier objects include the Messier catalog number, a common name if applicable, its parent constellation, the equatorial coordinates, and the magnitude. The star charts in the Constellations chapter help locate these objects.

Open Clusters

Open clusters contain up to a few thousand stars. As stars form in a giant molecular cloud, the new stars' radiation pressure drives the remaining cloud away. The result is a group of stars without the surrounding emission nebula. These stars are initially gravitationally bound, but they may have chaotic orbits that eject members from the group. Surviving clusters are therefore relatively young but older than stars embedded in emission nebulae.

However old the cluster is, the members have the same age in astronomical terms. Because open clusters contain stars of similar distance and age, they are excellent tools

Wikimedia Commons: NASA & ESA: public domain

for studying stellar evolution by mass and luminosity. The initial development of the H-R diagram utilized stars in open clusters.

The Messier catalog includes 26 objects classified as open clusters. Today, about 1,100 open clusters are known in the Milky Way galaxy. Given here is a list of four of the more prominent open clusters in the Messier catalog. They often appear to be a single dim star to the naked eye, except the Pleiades, which the eye resolves into several stars. Greek mythology names the seven sisters Sterope, Merope, Electra, Maia, Taygeta, Celaeno, and Alcyone, with their parents Atlas and Pleione. Galileo saw 36 stars in his small telescope. A pair of binoculars will do better. Telescopes reveal a blue nebulosity around the brighter stars, which is blue light from the hot young stars reflecting off dust, earning them the name reflection nebulae.

M	COMMON	CONST	RA	DEC	MAG
6	Butterfly Cluster	Scorpius	17^h 40^m 6^s	-32° 13'	4.2
7	Ptolemy Cluster	Scorpius	17^h 53^m 51^s	-34° 47' 34"	3.3
44	Praesepe (Beehive Cluster)	Cancer	8^h 40^m 24^s	19° 59'	3.7
45	Pleiades (Seven Sisters)	Taurus	3^h 47^m 24^s	24° 7'	1.6

Globular Clusters

Some of my favorite objects in the Milky Way are the beautiful but mysterious globular clusters. These spherically-shaped clusters contain hundreds of thousands to a million stars. Their name derives from the Latin globulus, a small sphere. Globulars exist in most large galaxies, scattered throughout their halos, rather than being confined to the disk where most stars reside. They are as old as the host galaxy itself. Globulars have no young stars. While globulars are old, all the stars formed are similar in age. They are low in heavy elements because they formed before the interstellar medium's enrichment by novae and supernovae. How globulars form is not fully understood. Over 150 globulars reside in the Milky Way. The Milky Way's sister, the Andromeda galaxy, contains over 500 globulars. Some giant galaxies have over 10,000 globulars.

Wikimedia Commons: NASA & ESA: public domain

Globulars are tightly bound gravitationally. They don't flatten into a disk because the entire system has little angular momentum. The individual stars have elliptical orbits of random inclination to the galactic plane. Imagine each star in an elliptical orbit around the entire system's center of mass. However, the high density of stars, and binary stars, cause significant interactions resulting in loops and other complex movements.

M	COMMON	CONST	RA	DEC	MAG
	ω Centauri	Centaurus	$13^h\ 26^m\ 47^s$	-47° 28' 46"	3.9
4		Scorpius	$16^h\ 23^m$	-26° 31' 33"	5.9
13	Hercules Cluster	Hercules	$16^h\ 41^m\ 41^s$	36° 27' 36"	5.8
22	Sagittarius Cluster	Sagittarius	$18^h\ 36^m\ 24^s$	-23° 54' 17"	5.1
92		Hercules	$17^h\ 17^m\ 8^s$	43° 8' 9"	6.3

The Messier catalog contains 29 globular clusters. Messier missed the two most beautiful globular clusters because they reside deep in the southern celestial hemisphere. They are Omega Centauri and 47 Tucanae, and both are easy naked-eye objects in dark skies. If you have a view clear to the southern horizon, Omega Centauri is visible in the southern United States. It appears as a fuzzy star. It's listed here with four other bright globulars in the Messier catalog.

Emission Nebulae

The Great Orion Nebula, described in the previous chapter, is an emission nebula. Emission nebulae are molecular clouds in star-birthing regions where hot young stars excite the gas that remains. There are seven emission nebulae in the Messier catalog, and the most outstanding is the Orion Nebula, M42. The nebula M43 is a catalog entry very close to M42 that Messier could have listed as a part of M42. Visually, M42 hints at being a faint and small nebulosity around the middle star in Orion's sword. Its form becomes evident in binoculars. In a telescope, it's spectacular. Pictured here is a composite photograph of the Eagle Nebula, M16, taken at the European Southern Observatory in Chile. Binoculars at least glimpse all of the Messier emission nebulae.

Wikimedia Commons: ESO: CC 4.0

M	COMMON	CONST	RA	DEC	MAG
8	Lagoon Nebula	Sagittarius	18^h 3^m 37^s	-24° 23' 12"	6.0
16	Eagle Nebula	Serpens	18^h 18^m 48^s	-13° 49'	6.0
17	Swan, or Omega Nebula	Sagittarius	18^h 20^m 26^s	-16° 10' 36"	6.0
20	Trifid Nebula	Sagittarius	18^h 2^m 23^s	-23° 1' 48"	6.3
42	Orion Nebula	Orion	5^h 35^m 17^s	-5° 23' 28"	4.0
43	De Mairan's Nebula	Orion	5^h 36^m 36^s	-5° 16'	9.0
78		Orion	5^h 46^m 47^s	00° 00' 50"	8.3

Planetary Nebulae

Planetary nebulae are also emission nebulae. They earned the name planetary nebulae because, in early telescopes, they resembled planets. However, these emission nebulae are not regions of star birth; but instead, they mark a star's death. When stars of moderate mass, such as our Sun, began to exhaust their hydrogen fuel, the outer layers swell into a red giant. An inner core of helium gravitationally

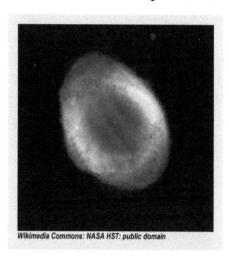

Wikimedia Commons: NASA HST: public domain

collapses until the helium's temperature becomes high enough to fuse into carbon and oxygen. The stellar wind blows the outer layers, representing a significant mass of the original star, outward into an expanding shell. The remaining star burns energetically, thus bathing the expanding ring with ultraviolet light causing it to glow. The surviving star is called a white dwarf. The expanding ring is typically somewhat spherical and symmetrical, causing a planet-like appearance. Planetary nebulae are, of course, much larger than planets, but their remoteness causes them to have an angular size similar to the planets. Early astronomers realized they weren't planets but named them for the appearance. Not all nebulae of this class are symmetrical nor appear planetary in shape.

Pictured here is the Ring Nebula in the constellation Lyra. This HST photograph also reveals the surviving white dwarf star in the very center. The spectrum of planetary nebulae shows the presence of carbon, oxygen, and nitrogen. While they don't contain the heaviest elements, planetary nebulae enrich the interstellar medium with moderate-weight elements. Astronomers have discovered about 3,000 planetary nebulae in the Milky Way. Compared to the number of stars, the relatively small number is because of their relatively short life span as they disperse.

All four planetary nebulae that Messier cataloged are listed here. Binoculars will reveal that the Ring Nebula is not a star, but it requires a telescope at a power over 25X to disclose the ring. Slightly brighter, and more obviously not a star is M27, the Dumbbell Nebula. A small telescope reveals it's not spherical but shaped more like - yeah, you can guess. A large telescope reveals faint areas that make the overall structure spherical. Large binoculars reveal M97, but it takes a telescope with an aperture of 10 inches or more for M97 to look like the face of an owl with two large dark areas that form the eyes.

M	COMMON	CONST	RA	DEC	MAG
27	Dumbbell Nebula	Vulpecula	19^h 59^m 36^s	22° 43' 16"	7.5
57	Ring Nebula	Lyra	18^h 53^m 35^s	33° 1' 45"	8.8
76	Little Dumbbell Nebula	Perseus	1^h 43^m 24^s	51° 34' 31"	10.1
97	Owl Nebula	Ursa Major	11^h 14^m 48^s	55° 1' 8"	9.9

Supernova Remnant

A supernova ejects most of the initial stellar mass. The resulting shell of material expands at velocities up to 10% of the speed of light, creating a shock wave as it slams into the surrounding interstellar medium. The shock initially causes x-ray radiation, and as the expansion slows, ionized hydrogen and oxygen glow in the reds and blues typical with these objects.

The ring eventually disperses and slows, and becomes undetectable. The oldest known supernova remnants are 20 to 100 thousand years old. This HST image shows the most recently observed remnant as it

Wikimedia Commons: NASA HST: public domain

appeared about 20 years after the supernova. It resides in the Large Magellanic Cloud, the Milky Way's nearby satellite galaxy. It occurred about 168,000 years ago, and light from it reached Earth on February 23, 1987. About three hours before the first light arrived at Earth, three different neutrino observatories detected neutrino particles. Those neutrinos started

Wikimedia Commons: NASA HST: public domain

their journey at the moment the stellar core collapsed. Theoretical models predict neutrinos carry 99% of the energy produced by the core collapse. By May, the supernova peaked at naked-eye visibility of magnitude three and later disappeared. The remaining neutron star was discovered in 2019 using the Atacama Large Millimeter Array radio telescope in Chile.

Nineteenth-century research by the French astronomer Jean-Baptiste Biot (1774 -1862) found an old but detailed Chinese writing that recorded a "guest star," a Chinese term for novas and supernovas. The supernova occurred in 1054, and twentieth-century research associated the location with the prominent Crab Nebula. Messier recorded M1 as the first entry and only supernova remnant in his catalog. This HST composite photograph of the Crab Nebula reveals an oval shape with remnant filaments of the star's atmosphere. At the center of the Crab Nebula is a pulsar that emits a pulse of radiation every 0.033 seconds.

Binoculars only hint at an oval form of dim light. It takes a telescope to reveal any detail or color.

M	COMMON	CONST	RA	DEC	MAG
1	Crab Nebula	Taurus	5^h 34^m 32^s	22° 00' 52"	8.4

Dark Nebulae

Wikimedia Commons: Z. Dischner: CC 2.0

If the Heavens reveals its secrets in light, the absence of light is also revealing. Consider this lovely composite picture of the Milky Way from the horizon in front of you to almost the horizon behind you at the top of the photo.

It reveals the dust lanes of the Milky Way. Stars concentrate in the Milky Way's disk, and so do the dust and gas from which they are born. The interstellar hydrogen and helium are nearly transparent, but the dust is not. As we look through the Milky Way arms, in places of higher concentration of dust, the light of distant stars is blocked. The individual stars that we see scattered through the Heavens are in our own Orion arm. The stars visible within the dust lanes are on our side of the dust lanes. The dust obscures the galactic center, complicating the study of the Milky Way core. Radio waves from sources within the core penetrate this dust, providing information about the core. Dust lanes are also prominent features of distant galaxies.

If you look closely at the center of the image of the Eagle Nebula in the section Emission Nebulae, you'll notice how the nebula got its name. A dark nebula with the unmistakable shape of an eagle blocks the light from the emission nebula behind it. These dark nebulae often associate with emission nebulae, as in the Great Orion Nebula. These dark nebulae are different from the dark clouds in the arms of the Milky Way. They are smaller and denser and often have more distinct edges because of that density. The Dutch-American astronomer Bart Bok (1906 – 1983) first noted these dense dark clouds, now called Bok globules, in the 1940s. Infrared and millimeter-wave telescopes reveal Bok globules contain protostars, stars in the process of forming. It's believed these high-density molecular clouds typically create multiple-star systems.

Messier didn't include dark nebulae in his catalog because they wouldn't be confused as comets. Bok nebulae require a telescope to view, but dust lanes hide portions of the Milky Way from view in dark skies. Just as the ancients imagined animals and mythical gods in constellations of stars, the Incas and aboriginal Australians imagined animals and objects in the Milky Way's dark lanes, which are more prominent in southern skies. The Coalsack in the southern constellation Crux is perhaps the most pronounced dark nebula, but northern views can see the Great Rift in the Milky Way stretching from Cygnus to Sagittarius. In dark skies, the naked eye reveals dark nebulae throughout both the Summer and Winter Milky Way.

Other Catalogues

In 1786, the German astronomer and composer William Herschel (1738 – 1822) published his Catalogue of Nebulae and Clusters of Stars containing 1000 objects. While compiling his catalog in 1781, he discovered the planet Uranus. Herschel's sister and astronomer, Caroline, assisted with compiling the catalog. Herschel's son, John, joined the effort and continued after his father's death. John's catalog reached 5,079 entries by 1864.

Following the Herschel family lead, the Danish-British astronomer John Louis Emil Dreyer (1852 – 1926) published the New General Catalogue of Nebulae and Clusters of Stars (NGC) with 7,840 objects in 1888, followed by another 5,386 objects in a supplemental Index Catalogues (IC) in 1895 and 1908 with 5,386 objects. Professional and amateur astronomers use the NGC and IC catalogs to this day.

Automated Earth-based and space telescopes have created multiple catalogs, some with nearly a billion entries. Specialists on various astronomical objects have compiled many hundreds of catalogs covering specific classes of objects. Whatever your interest, whether it be double stars, planetary nebulae, nova, etc., there is a catalog for you.

8 Constellations

The constellations are more than connect-the-dot figures. Our culture embeds their names in art and aircraft, cities and companies, magazines and motion pictures, buildings and brews, ships and songs, literally anything that needs a name. More than that, as you get to know them, they become your friends. Their appearance evokes memories and ushers in the seasons. This chapter covers a few of the more prominent constellations with stories, charts, and denizens within their borders.

History

The constellations recognized today are descendants of many cultures. The Greeks adopted many Mesopotamian and Babylonian constellations, and Ptolemy listed 48 of the currently recognized constellations in his *Almagest*. While cultures worldwide certainly had myths and interpretations, the scientific advances in Greece and the later European Scientific Revolution influenced the constellation names' ultimate acceptance. Europeans added names in the 16th and 17th centuries and later traveled to the Southern Hemisphere to

Wikimedia Commons: T. Bronger: public domain

chart more constellations in the 18th century. This constellation figure of Orion is from *Firmamentum Sobiescianum* by Johannes Hevelius (1611 – 1687). In 1922, the IAU officially accepted the current list of constellations.

The 88 Constellations

The following table lists the IAU recognized 88 constellations. In his 2nd century Almagest, Ptolemy named the constellations listed with a (P) in the table. In 1592 and 1613, the Dutch-Flemish astronomer Petrus Plancius (1552 – 1622) named the constellations marked (N). Constellations identified with a (U) are from Uranometria, a star atlas published in 1603, which included Ptolemy's constellations. Hevelius named the constellations marked with an (H). The French astronomer Nicolas-Louis de Lacaille (1713 – 1762) traveled to the Cape of Good Hope in the Southern Hemisphere and charted the constellations identified with an (L) in his 1763 catalog.

The table lists the constellations in alphabetical order along with the IAU abbreviation. Not all constellations can be seen from all points on Earth, but only by an observer on the equator. All observers can see at least a portion of constellations lying on the celestial equator. The fourth column indicates the latitude range where the entire constellation can be seen. For example, Orion straddles the celestial equator and can be seen from latitudes 85°N to 75°S. Observers in the Northern Hemisphere may not be able to observe southern constellations. For example, Crux, the Southern Cross, can't be seen north of latitude 20°N.

The final column is the month the constellation culminates at midnight for Northern Hemisphere observers. Culmination is the passage across the meridian, a great circle from the north celestial pole to the observer's southern horizon. When a constellation culminates at midnight, it rises in the east at sunset, sets in the west at sunrise, so it's visible all night.

CONSTELLATION	ABRr	MEANING	LATITUDE	CUL
Andromeda (P)	And	chained maiden	90°N–40°S	Oct
Antlia (L)	Ant	air pump	45°N–90°S	Mar
Apus (U)	Aps	bird-of-paradise	5°N–90°S	Jun
Aquarius (P)	Aqr	water-bearer	65°N–90°S	Sep
Aquila (P)	Aql	eagle	90°N–75°S	Aug
Ara (P)	Ara	altar	25°N–90°S	Jul
Aries (P)	Ari	ram	90°N–60°S	Nov
Auriga (P)	Aur	charioteer	90°N–40°S	Dec
Boötes (P)	Boo	herdsman	90°N–50°S	May
Caelum (L)	Cae	chisel	40°N–90°S	Dec
Camelopardalis (N)	Cam	giraffe	90°N–10°S	Jan
Cancer (P)	Cnc	crab	90°N–60°S	Feb
Canes Venatici (H)	CVn	hunting dogs	90°N–40°S	May
Canis Major (P)	CMa	greater dog	60°N–90°S	Jan
Canis Minor (P)	CMi	lesser dog	90°N–75°S	Jan
Capricornus (P)	Cap	sea goat	60°N–90°S	Sep
Carina (L)	Car	keel	20°N–90°S	Feb
Cassiopeia (P)	Cas	Cassiopeia	90°N–20°S	Oct
Centaurus (P)	Cen	centaur	25°N–90°S	May
Cepheus (P)	Cep	Cepheus	90°N–10°S	Sep
Cetus (P)	Cet	sea monster	70°N–90°S	Nov
Chamaeleon (U)	Cha	chameleon	0°–90°S	Mar
Circinus (L)	Cir	drafting compass	30°N–90°S	May
Columba (N)	Col	dove	45°N–90°S	Dec
Coma Berenices (U)	Com	Berenice's hair	90°N–70°S	Apr
Corona Australis (P)	CrA	Southern Crown	40°N–90°S	Jul
Corona Borealis (P)	CrB	Northern Crown	90°N–50°S	Jun
Corvus (P)	Crv	crow	60°N–90°S	Apr
Crater (P)	Crt	cup	65°N–90°S	Apr
Crux (U)	Cru	Southern Cross	20°N–90°S	Apr
Cygnus (P)	Cyg	swan	90°N–40°S	Aug
Delphinus (P)	Del	dolphin	90°N–70°S	Aug
Dorado (U)	Dor	dolphin fish	20°N–90°S	Dec
Draco (P)	Dra	dragon	90°N–15°S	Jul
Equuleus (P)	Equ	pony	90°N–80°S	Sep

CONSTELLATION	ABRr	MEANING	LATITUDE	CUL
Eridanus (P)	Eri	river	32°N–90°S	Nov
Fornax (L)	For	furnace	50°N–90°S	Nov
Gemini (P)	Gem	twins	90°N–60°S	Jan
Grus (U)	Gru	crane	34°N–90°S	Sep
Hercules (P)	Her	Hercules	90°N–50°S	Jul
Horologium (L)	Hor	pendulum clock	30°N–90°S	Nov
Hydra (P)	Hya	Hydra	54°N–83°S	Mar
Hydrus (U)	Hyi	water snake	8°N–90°S	Nov
Indus (U)	Ind	Indian	15°N–90°S	Sep
Lacerta (H)	Lac	lizard	90°N–40°S	Sep
Leo (P)	Leo	lion	90°N–65°S	Mar
Leo Minor (H)	LMi	lesser lion	90°N–45°S	Mar
Lepus (P)	Lep	hare	63°N–90°S	Dec
Libra (P)	Lib	balance	65°N–90°S	Jun
Lupus (P)	Lup	wolf	35°N–90°S	Jun
Lynx (H)	Lyn	lynx	90°N–55°S	Jan
Lyra (P)	Lyr	lyre	90°N–40°S	Jul
Mensa (L)	Men	Table Mountain	4°N–90°S	Dec
Microscopium (L)	Mic	microscope	45°N–90°S	Aug
Monoceros (N)	Mon	unicorn	75°N–90°S	Jan
Musca (U)	Mus	fly	10°N–90°S	Apr
Norma (L)	Nor	level	30°N–90°S	Jun
Octans (L)	Oct	octant	0°- 90°S	Sep
Ophiuchus (P)	Oph	serpent-bearer	80°N–80°S	Jul
Orion (P)	Ori	hunter	85°N–75°S	Dec
Pavo (U)	Pav	peacock	30°N–90°S	Aug
Pegasus (P)	Peg	winged horse	90°N–60°S	Sep
Perseus (P)	Per	Perseus	90°N–35°S	Nov
Phoenix (U)	Phe	phoenix	32°N–80°S	Oct
Pictor (L)	Pic	easel	26°N–90°S	Dec
Pisces (P)	Psc	fishes	90°N–65°S	Oct
Piscis Austrinus (P)	PsA	southern fish	55°N–90°S	Sep
Puppis (L)	Pup	poop deck	40°N–90°S	Jan
Pyxis (L)	Pyx	compass	50°N–90°S	Feb

CONSTELLATION	ABRr	MEANING	LATITUDE	CUL
Reticulum (L)	Rei	Eyepiece graticule	23°N–90°S	Nov
Sagitta (P)	Sge	arrow	90°N–70°S	Aug
Sagittarius (P)	Sgr	archer	55°N–90°S	Aug
Scorpius (P)	Sco	scorpion	40°N–90°S	Jun
Sculptor (L)	Scl	sculptor	50°N–90°S	Oct
Scutum (H)	Sct	shield	80°N–90°S	Jul
Serpens (P)	Ser	snake	80°N–80°S	Jun
Sextans (H)	Sex	sextant	80°N–90°S	Mar
Taurus (P)	Tau	bull	90°N–65°S	Dec
Telescopium (L)	Tel	telescope	40°N–90°S	Aug
Triangulum (P)	Tri	triangle	90°N–60°S	Nov
Triangulum Australe (U)	TrA	southern triangle	25°N–90°S	Jun
Tucana (U)	Tuc	toucan	25°N–90°S	Oct
Ursa Major (P)	Uma	great bear	90°N–30°S	Mar
Ursa Minor (P)	Umi	lesser bear	90°N–10°S	Jun
Vela (L)	Vel	sails	30°N–90°S	Feb
Virgo (P)	Vir	virgin	80°N–80°S	May
Volans (U)	Vol	flying fish	15°N–90°S	Jan
Vulpecula (H)	Vul	fox	90°N–55°S	Aug

Many of the constellations require a stretch of the imagination to associate the star pattern with its namesake. The stars in some of the constellations are dim and unremarkable. Other constellations contain several brighter stars, and the association is apparent, such as the scorpion, the lion, the hunter, the dragon, and the swan. Some names such as the teapot and big dipper are popularizations of asterisms of a portion of the constellation. The following pages describe a few of the 88 constellations listed in order of the date of culmination.

Gemini

Gemini is Latin for twins; in this case, the twin half-brothers Castor and Pollux of Greek mythology born to Leda, a Spartan queen. I'll leave it to you to figure that one out. Pollux was the son of Zeus, an immortal. When Castor died, Pollux begged Zeus to make Castor immortal also,

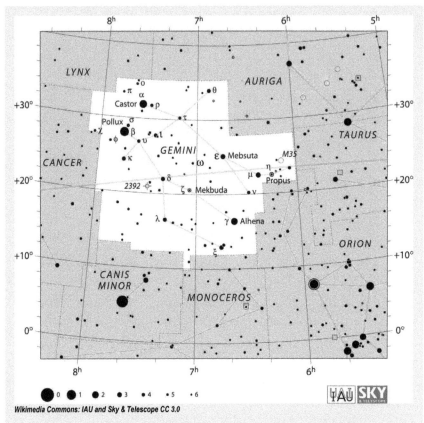

which Zeus did by placing them together in the Heavens.
Gemini bisects the ecliptic and is the northernmost
member of the zodiac. The Sun transits Gemini in May and
June, so it culminates at midnight in January. Gemini is
northeast of Orion. The bright twin stars, Castor and
Pollux, shine at magnitudes 1.58 and 1.15, respectively.
Castor is a sextuple star system. It consists of three sets of
double stars. Two sets are bright, and a dim set is an
eclipsing binary. Binoculars do not resolve these stars.

One of the more pleasing clusters in the Winter sky is
the open star cluster M35. It's just northwest of the lower
right foot of Gemini. In binoculars, M35 appears as a
handful of bright stars over a dim background of hundreds

OBJECT	MAG	DESCRIPTION
M35	5.1	Barely visible naked eye. Very nice in binoculars.
NGC2392	8	Eskimo Nebula. Just discernable as a disk in large binoculars

of unresolved stars. Gemini also contains an excellent example of a planetary nebula. NGC2392, the Eskimo Nebula. It's just discernable as a blue disk in large binoculars. A small telescope reveals the central star. This is a picture of the Eskimo Nebula taken with an extremely large amateur telescope.

Wikimedia Commons: Jschulman555: CC 4.0

Ursa Major

Ursa Major, or Great Bear, is also known as the Big Dipper, a name justly derived from its shape as a ladle. The dipper forms only a portion of the Great Bear, as seen in the chart. Seven of the brighter stars define the big dipper, the lower body, and the bear's tail. You can visualize a bear by imagining the dipper being the back of its body and the tail, the star Muscida the nose, the stars θ and κ as the front legs, and the left lower stars the back legs.

The dipper handle's middle star is the famous double Mizar and Alcor, which keen eyesight resolves. Whether Mizar and Alcor are gravitationally bound is uncertain. Spectroscopic studies have revealed that Mizar is four stars and Alcor is two, so it may be a system of six stars.

The Big Dipper is an essential signpost for the North Star, Polaris. Polaris is only the second magnitude. To find Polaris extend a line from Merak to Dubhe. Using prominent stars to locate celestial objects is a common technique. Amateur astronomers call this star hopping.

As the seasons and evenings progress, the stars rotate counter-clockwise around Polaris. This movement is westward for most stars, but looking northward, stars

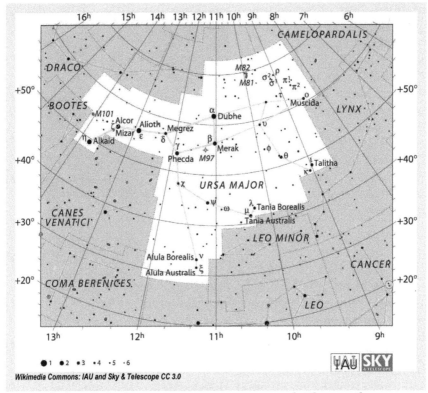

below Polaris appear to move eastward. The southern extent of the Big Dipper's handle is about declination 49°N so that for observers north of latitude 41°N (90° - 49°), the Big Dipper never drops below the northern horizon. It never sets and is said to be circumpolar.

Ursa Major culminates in March, giving observers not too far south of the equator a chance to see it. It also crosses the meridian six months later, but it's then at its lowest elevation and not well placed for observing.

The galaxies M82/81 may be found by star-hopping from Phecda to Dubhe. M82 and M81 are about the same distance from Dubhe as Dubhe is from Phecda. M81 is

OBJECT	MAG	DESCRIPTION
M81	6.9	Oval in binoculars.
M82	8.4	Dimmer than M82. A peculiar galaxy with a cigar shape.

brighter, and binoculars reveal it's an oval. M82 is visible
in binoculars, but a telescope is required to view the dust
lanes. The galaxies M101 and M108 and the Owl Nebula
need a telescope for best viewing.

Leo

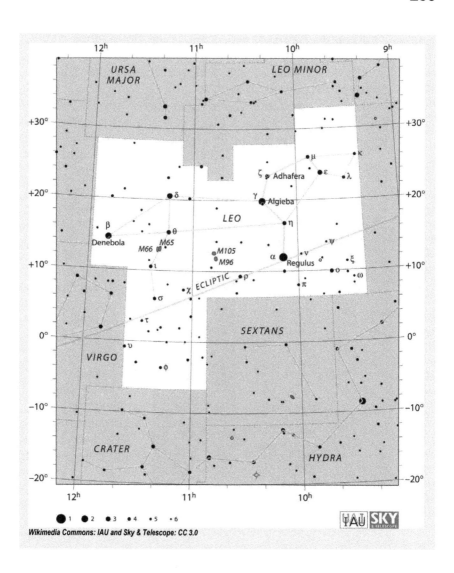

Wikimedia Commons: IAU and Sky & Telescope: CC 3.0

Another constellation culminating in March is Leo, the Lion. It lies on the ecliptic and is a member of the zodiac. It's one of the original 48 constellations in Ptolemy's *Almagest*. The Sun transits Leo in July and August. The brightest star in the constellation is Regulus at magnitude 1.4. Regulus is a quadruple system, and binoculars easily reveal it as a double. Regulus is at the base of an asterism called The Sickle that includes η, Algieba, Adhafera, μ, and ε. The Sickle forms the lion's chest and mane, and the triangle, which includes Denebola, forms the haunches of the lion. These bright stars make Leo unmistakable in the south in March.

Regulus, Latin for little king, is the closest bright star to the ecliptic. Regulus is often occulted by the Moon, rarely asteroids, and very rarely by Mercury and Venus. The last occult by Venus was in 1959.

Denebola and Arcturus in the constellation Bootes, and Spica in the constellation Virgo, form a nearly equilateral triangle called the Spring Triangle.

The Messier galaxies M65, M66, M95, M96, and M105 reside in Leo. Binoculars detect these galaxies, but

telescopes reveal some detail. This image of M96 by the HST clearly shows H II star-birthing clouds and dust lanes. If you want to try for a galaxy in Leo, perhaps the most interesting, although dim, is an oval-shaped galaxy that Messier missed. NGC2903 lies just 1.5° degrees south of λ.

Wikimedia Commons: ESA & HST: CC 4.0

Ursa Minor

Ursa Minor, the Lesser Bear, includes the pole star Polaris. It has only three stars at magnitude three or brighter and needs dark skies to see the dipper asterism with the handle bent backward. Polaris is the star at the end of the handle, and once you know how to find Polaris using the Big Dipper, then finding the Little Dipper is easier.

The Little Dipper culminates in June with the dipper above Polaris. It's shown in this chart during lower culmination, upside down, and six months later. The Little Dipper is circumpolar for viewers north of 20°N latitude.

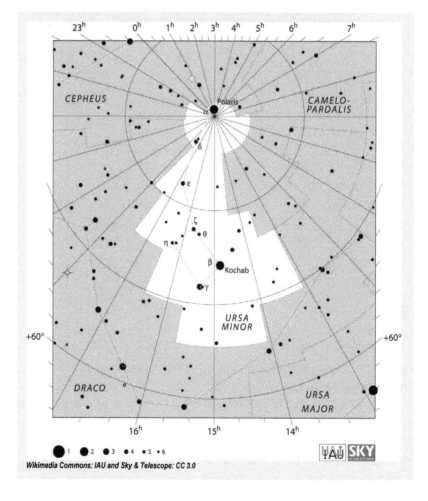

Scorpius

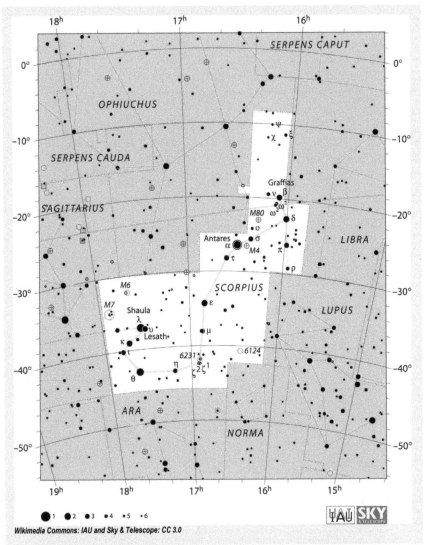

Scorpius, the scorpion, is the southernmost constellation of the zodiac. One of Ptolemy's original 48 constellations, it culminates in late June and resembles its namesake well. The bright red star Antares is the heart of the scorpion. The stars β, δ, and π are the head and pinchers. The tail is well-formed, and λ with υ makes a convincing stinger.

Antares is a red supergiant and one of the largest observable stars. It's about 900 times the diameter of the Sun. It's also highly luminous, but since it's 550 ly away, it's only the fifteenth brightest star in the night sky. The name probably derives from the ancient Greek meaning "equal to Mars" since its color and brightness are similar to Mars. Antares brightness varies a little and somewhat erratically, but you may count on it to beat as the heart of Scorpius.

The Sun transits the boundaries of Scorpius in about seven days in late November and early December. The rest of the month, the Sun transits Ophiuchus, which astrologers don't recognize as part of the zodiac. The other bad news for astrology's legitimacy is that it considers two zodiacs: the tropical zodiac and the sidereal zodiac. Take your pick, depending on which soothsayer you care to believe.

The tail of Scorpius lies in the richest part of the Summer Milky Way. It's as if Scorpius is trying to outrun it. Scorpius is home to several objects for binoculars and telescopes, including four in the Messier catalog. Here is a list of objects and a description of their appearance in binoculars. Of course, they are more stunning in a telescope. NGC6281 is not on the chart. It's about 1/3 of the way from NGC6231 toward the stinger stars. On a fine mid-Summer evening, grab whatever optical glass you have, head for dark skies, and find a clear view of the southern horizon.

OBJECT	MAG	DESCRIPTION
M4	5.9	Small fuzzy globe. Stars are resolved only in very large binoculars.
M6	4.2	Open cluster with two "butterfly" wings of about 30 stars. Nice.
M7	3.3	Open cluster with about 30 yellow and blue stars.
M80	7.9	Fuzzy globe with a brighter center. Unresolved in binoculars.
NGC6124	5.8	Open cluster of about 20 stars. Brighter stars in the middle.
NGC6231	2.6	Beautiful open cluster with many bright stars. Stars everywhere.
NGC6281	5.4	Open cluster with 7 or 8 stars.

Hercules

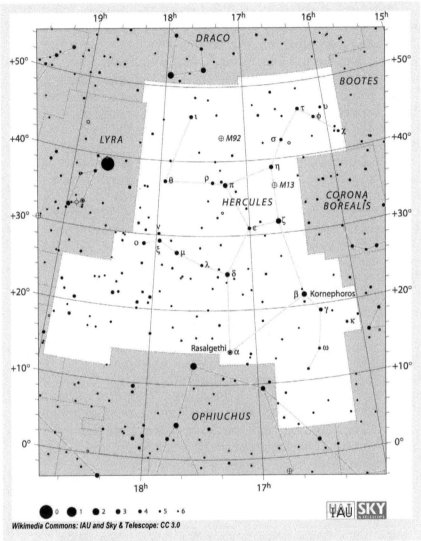

Hercules is another original constellation in Ptolemy's *Almagest*. Hercules is a Roman adaptation of the Greek Heracles, who was the son of Zeus and Alcmene. Hercules survived many trials and was known for his strength and as a champion of the oppressed. In the sky, Hercules is on his knees. In the chart, he is upside down. However, when he culminates at midnight in June, he is right-side up high above Polaris. Hercules' brightest star, Rasalgethi, α Her, is an excellent telescopic double but unresolved in binoculars. It's also a variable star that fades just less than a magnitude from its brightest magnitude 3.1.

Wikimedia Commons: S. Leach/A. Block Mt. Lemmon SkyCenter: CC 4.0

The globular cluster M13 is the finest globular in northern skies. It's barely naked-eye visible in ideal conditions at magnitude 6. It's a fuzzy glow in binoculars, and a telescope resolves some of its stars. Another fine globular is M92 northeast of M13.

OBJECT	MAG	DESCRIPTION
M13	5.8	Finest globular cluster in northern skies, although unresolved in binos
M92	6.3	Smaller and dimmer than M13. A faint glow in binoculars

Lyra

Lyra, Latin for lyre, is a small constellation that culminates in late July or early August. In mythology, it's the lyre of Orpheus, the musician and poet. His lyre was so melodious it could charm inanimate objects. Orpheus accompanied Jason and quelled the Sirens to save the Argonauts.

Lyra is one of Ptolemy's original 48 constellations. Lyra's parallelogram consisting of ζ, δ, ε, and β is easy to find once the bright star Vega is found. Although it's slightly variable, Vega functions as the reference star at magnitude zero. Vega is a star in the Summer Triangle and the star featured in the movie *Contact*. Vega was the pole star in 12,000 BC and will be again in 14,000 AD.

Despite its small size, Lyra contains binary and variable stars of many types, so astronomers constantly study its stars. Lyra has two Messier objects. The Ring Nebula, M57,

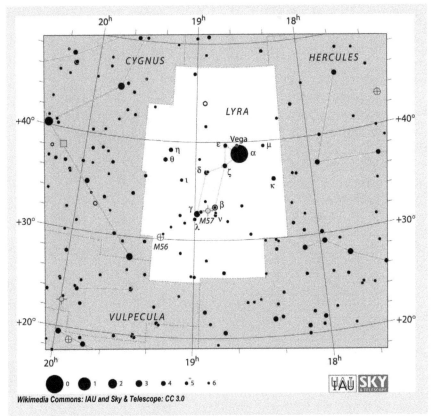

Wikimedia Commons: IAU and Sky & Telescope: CC 3.0

was described earlier. It's visible in binoculars but requires a telescope to see the ring. The globular cluster M56 is a fuzzy star in binoculars but shows many bright stars and more small stars in large amateur telescopes.

The famous Double-Double, ε Lyra, also described earlier, is a double in binoculars and a double-double in 3-inch and larger telescopes.

OBJECT	MAG	DESCRIPTION
M57	8.8	Ring Nebula. Visible in binoculars but requires a telescope to see a ring
M56	8.3	Globular cluster that appears like a dim, fuzzy star in binoculars
ε Lyra	5/5.2	Double-Double. A double in binos. Quadruple in 3" and larger telescopes

Sagittarius

Sagittarius is Latin for "archer," and mythology imagined it as a centaur pulling back a bow. Another of Ptolemy's 48 original constellations. Sagittarius rests on the ecliptic and is the ninth tropical astrological sign from November 23 to December 21. Sagittarius culminates at midnight in late July. On the western edge of this large constellation lies an asterism called The Teapot. While I

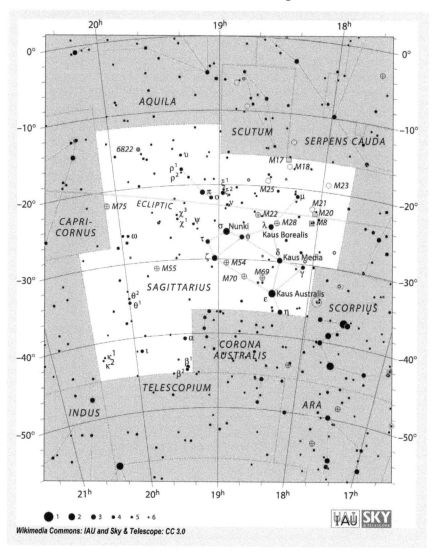

don't see the centaur, the teapot is unmistakable. It makes this southern Summer constellation easy to spot. The center of the Milky Way is in Sagittarius.

Sagittarius is a treasure-trove of Heavenly objects. It has 14 Messier objects. M8, the Lagoon Nebula, is an emission nebula that is naked-eye visible, a Summer treat that rivals the Winter's Great Orion Nebula. Binoculars reveal a large glow bisected by a dark nebula, the lagoon. The Omega Nebula, M17, is another beautiful emission nebula. Telescopes offer a better view of the dimmer M20.

Open clusters include M18, M21, M23, and M25. M18 is not particularly impressive, while M21 and M23 are much more stunning in binoculars. The open clusters M24 and M25 are naked-eye visible. M24 is a concentration of stars in the Milky Way that is three times larger than the Moon. It could hardly be mistaken for a comet. Some refer to M24 as the Small Sagittarius Star Cloud. This IAU/Sky and Telescope chart doesn't include it. It's 1.5° NE of M25. M24 appears just as Messier described it, so it was not a mistake, just a strange inclusion in the catalog. On the northwestern side of M24 is the dark nebula Barnard 92. Other less prominent dark nebulae reside in front of M24.

The globular clusters M28, M54, M55, M69, M70, and M75 appear small and dim. Of these, perhaps M75 is the most interesting in binoculars. It appears as a small round glow, brighter towards the core.

OBJECT	MAG	DESCRIPTION
M8	6.0	Nebula with detail in binoculars. Includes open cluster NGC 6530.
M17	6.0	Beautiful emission nebula
M21	6.5	Lots of stars in an open cluster. Pretty.
M23	6.9	Large area of a few resolved and many unresolved stars.
M24	4.6	See text.
M25	4.6	Open cluster with about a dozen stars resolved in binoculars.
M75	9.2	Small and dim globular that is brighter in the core.

Cygnus

The Summer constellation Cygnus is easily recognized as its official namesake, a swan, or its popular moniker, the Northern Cross. In Greek mythology, Cygnus is a different swan depending on your story of choice. As a swan flying southwest, imagine the star Deneb is the tail, Albireo is the head, while ζ and κ are the wingtips. Alternatively, the

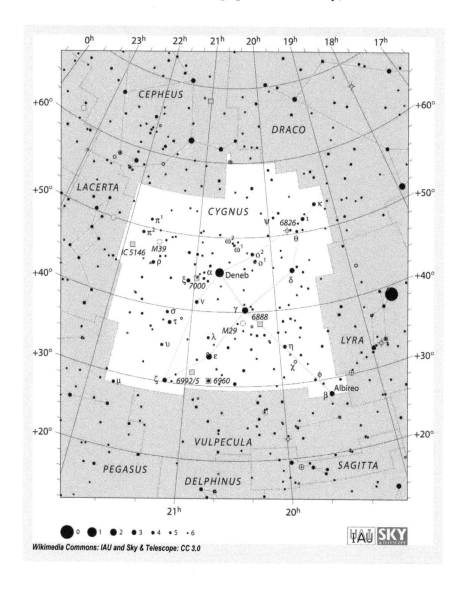

brighter ε and δ form the wings. The stars ε, δ, Deneb, and Albireo form the easily recognized Northern Cross. Deneb is one of the stars in the Summer triangle.

Cygnus culminates at midnight high overhead in August and is easy to spot in the middle of the Milky Way that spans the sky from the southwest to the northeast. Cygnus includes two Messier objects, five NGC objects, and other interesting binocular gems. NGC6960, 6992, and 6995 are all a part of the Veil Nebula, the large and diffuse remnant of an ancient supernova. It's visible in amateur telescopes equipped with a nebula filter. Pictured here is NGC 7000, the North American Nebula, another dim object, but possible with binoculars or naked-eye in ideal conditions.

61 Cyg is a very close double in all but higher-power binoculars. It's the small star that forms a triangle with δ and τ Cyg to the east. Importantly, this star was the first star to have its parallax measured. In 1804, astronomers noticed it had a significant proper motion. In 1838, the German astronomer and mathematician Friedrich Bessel (1784 – 1846) measured the parallax and determined the star to be 10.4 ly distant, close to the current value of 11.4 ly.

OBJECT	MAG	DESCRIPTION
M29	7.1	Small sparse open cluster.
M39	5.5	Naked-eye visibility in ideal conditions. Many stars in binoculars.
NGC6826	8.8	Obvious planetary with a tiny blue glow in large binoculars.
NGC6888	7.4	Emission nebula that requires very large binoculars.
NGC7000	4.0	Spread over a large area, it's difficult in binoculars and telescopes.
NGC7039	7.6	Large open cluster with several resolved stars.
Albireo	3.0	Close double split into brilliant yellow and beautiful sapphire stars.
χ	3.6 – 14	Variable in 200 days from easy naked-eye to invisible in binoculars.
61 Cyg	5.2,6.0	See text

Pegasus

An Autumn constellation is Pegasus, named for the winged horse of Greek mythology. Poseidon sired, and the snake-haired Medusa foaled Pegasus. Born after Perseus decapitated Medusa, Pegasus ascended to the heavens to be obedient to Zeus, King of the Gods.

Pegasus is one of Ptolemy's 48 constellations. Pegasus covers a large area of sky and is the seventh-largest constellation in total area. The asterism of stars that make the constellation so easy to recognize is the Great Square of Pegasus. The Great Square is an almost perfect square of four stars. One of the Great Square's four stars, Alpheratz, is in the constellation Andromeda, but let's ignore that little detail. The constellation Andromeda is northeast of Pegasus. Much of Pegasus is to the west of the Great Square, on the other side from Andromeda. For us,

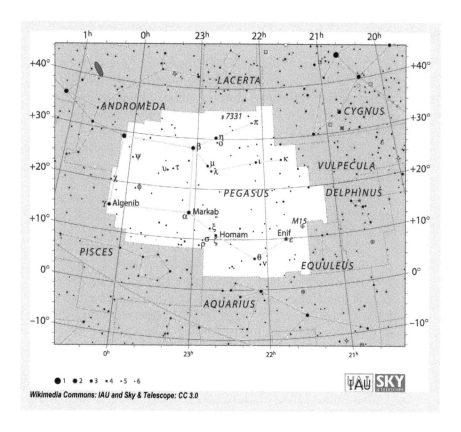

Wikimedia Commons: IAU and Sky & Telescope: CC 3.0

Pegasus (a stallion) is flying upside down with his head southwest of the Great Square. Flying upside down is not a problem for the horse of a god. If a horse flying upside down bothers you, you can lay on the ground with your feet pointing north and then look up. Pegasus culminates overhead at midnight in late September.

The globular cluster Messier 15 lies at the western edge of Pegasus. It's an unresolved globular fuzzy patch of dim light in binoculars. The plane of galaxy NGC7331 is oriented about 45° to us, and binoculars reveal the resulting oval shape as a dim patch of light. NGC7331 is unusual in that the core is rotating in the opposite direction of the disk.

OBJECT	MAG	DESCRIPTION
M15	6.2	Small fuzzy globe in binoculars. Stars resolved only in telescopes.
NGC7331	10.4	Spiral galaxy easily noticed as oval in binoculars.

Andromeda

Andromeda is another of Ptolemy's original 48 constellations. In mythology, as a sacrifice to save his kingdom, King Cephus chained his daughter Andromeda to rocks to be fed to the sea serpent Cetus. Fortunately, the hero Perseus saved the day (trumpets, please).

Andromeda is easily found beginning with the northeastern star, Alpheratz, of the Great Square of Pegasus. Alpheratz is actually in the constellation Andromeda which extends northward and both east and west of Alpheratz. Andromeda culminates overhead at midnight in late October.

Andromeda is home to M31, the Andromeda Galaxy. It's the most distant object visible to the naked eye. It's sometimes referred to as our sister galaxy because it's the closest galaxy similar to our Milky Way. It contains a trillion (10^{12}) stars, perhaps several times as many stars as in the Milky Way. In many respects, the Andromeda Galaxy is easier to study than our own since dust obscures much of our galaxy.

When I was a boy, the estimated distance to the Andromeda Galaxy was two million light-years. Fifty years

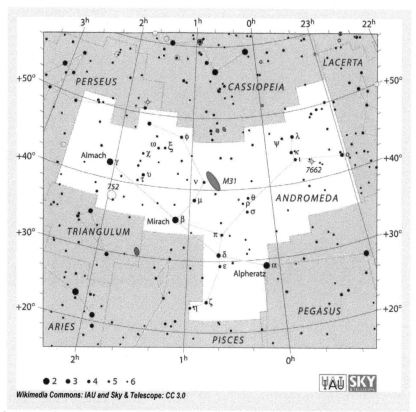

of research using ground and space-based telescopes, worth billions of dollars, has revised the estimated distance upwards to 2.5 million light-years. The light from the Andromeda Galaxy has traveled 2.5 million years. What we see is unimaginably old and distant.

In very dark skies, you can barely see the Andromeda Galaxy with unaided eyes. Amazingly, its angular extent is larger than the Moon, but it's so faint that all you see is the small, bright center. It looks like a dim, fuzzy star. Begin with Alpheratz (α And) and find the horn-shaped asterism containing δ, π, β, and μ And. Just northwest of μ is ν And, and just west of ν is the Andromeda Galaxy. The first time it's tricky to find. Once you learn what it looks like, it's much easier to find and beautiful in binoculars. This picture also includes M32 (above) and M110 (below). M31 is too large to entirely fit in the view of a telescope at high power.

OBJECT	MAG	DESCRIPTION
M31	3.44	Visible naked eye. By far the best galaxy in any optical instrument.
NGC752	5.7	Large open cluster with some stars resolved in binoculars.
NGC7662	8.6	Planetary nebula appears stellar in binoculars. Telescopes reveal disk.

Cassiopeia

Cassiopeia includes an easily recognized asterism that looks like a "W" when it's below Polaris and an "M" when it's above Polaris. This asterism is circumpolar for observers north of 35°N latitude. Cassiopeia culminates above Polaris just after Andromeda.

In mythology, Cassiopeia was the vain queen who boasted about her beauty and that of her daughter, which got Andromeda chained to the rocks. It also got Cassiopeia placed in the sky to whirl around Polaris and spend half her time upside down.

Cassiopeia is a treasure trove of open clusters, including M52, M103, NGC457, and NGC663. Binoculars

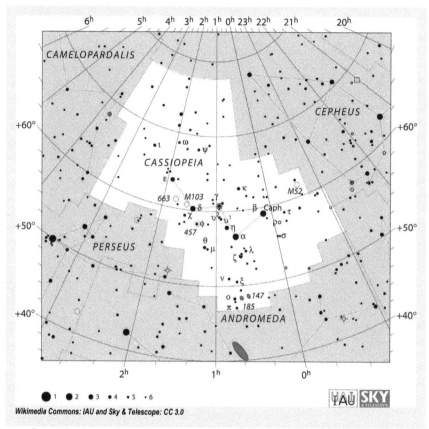

Wikimedia Commons: IAU and Sky & Telescope: CC 3.0

resolve a few stars in M52 and NGC663. It requires giant binoculars to resolve stars in M103, but a string of four unrelated stars to the southeast adds to its beauty.

The most interesting is perhaps NGC457. Binoculars resolve two stars while a telescope reveals a rich cluster of stars forming the body, with the two bright stars the eyes of an owl or the movie character ET. Thus, it's also referred to as the Owl or ET Cluster.

OBJECT	MAG	DESCRIPTION
M52	5.0	Compact open cluster with a few stars resolved in binoculars.
M103	7.4	Easily visible but too compact for binoculars to resolve.
NGC457	6.4	The ET cluster, after the movie character.
NGC663	7.1	Hundreds of stars but binoculars resolve only a few.

Perseus

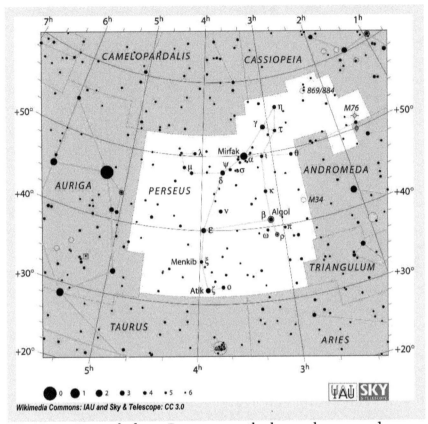

Wikimedia Commons: IAU and Sky & Telescope: CC 3.0

In mythology, Perseus was the hero who rescued Andromeda by killing Cetus with his sword. It must have been a sharp sword because he also used it to decapitate the wicked Medusa. He married Andromeda, they had six children, lived happily ever after, and died of old age.

Perseus culminates at midnight in late November or early December. Your guide is the brightest star Mirfak, between the bright star Capella to the east and Andromeda to the west. The eclipsing binary, Algol, written about in Chapter 6, is the second brightest star in Perseus when not eclipsed. Perseus contains Messier 34, a beautiful open cluster with resolved stars in binoculars and a faint background glow from hundreds of unresolved stars.

But by far, the gem in Perseus is NGC 869 and 884, the Double Cluster. They are just naked-eye visible in dark skies as an elongated blur of light. In binoculars, they are a stunning display of two sets of stars.

Wikimedia Commons: Andrew Cooper: CC 3.0

Perseus is also the home of the radiant of the Perseids meteor shower around August 12 each year. If that time of the month is near the dark of the Moon, you won't want to miss it. The radiant is near the star η PER, but after midnight, the whole sky will be a theater of shooting stars.

OBJECT	MAG	DESCRIPTION
M34	5.5	Binoculars resolve many stars with background glow from others.
NGC869/884	3.7	The Double Cluster. Stunning display of stars. Naked eye visible.

Taurus

Identifying the constellation with a bull is one of the oldest associations in the heavens, dating as far back as 5000 BC and perhaps to cave paintings around 15,000 BC. Many cultures associate these stars with a bull, including Babylonian, Egyptian, Greek, Druid, and later western culture. In Greek mythology, Zeus became Taurus the bull to abduct the princess Europa, who rode away upon his back.

Taurus is a constellation of the ecliptic and the tropical zodiac sign from April 20 to May 20. It's easily spotted above and to the right of the great constellation Orion. The most notable feature of Taurus is a vee-shaped asterism of five stars, including the bright red star Aldebaran, the bull's bloodshot eye. The five-star asterism represents the

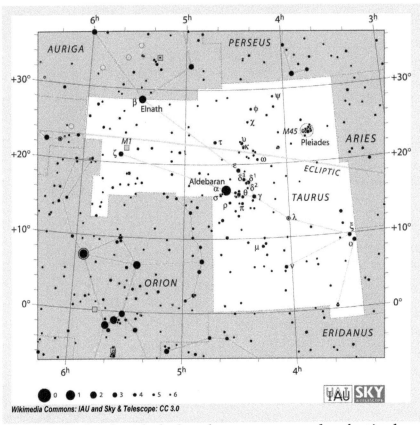

bull's head, with the long horns represented at the tips by two stars to the upper left.

Taurus contains the prominent star clusters Hyades and Pleiades. The Hyades includes the five stars forming Taurus' vee and around two hundred other stars best viewed in binoculars. The other cluster, M45, the Pleiades, is often called the Seven Sisters. In binoculars, many more than seven stars are visible. The stars of the Pleiades formed relatively recently, within the last 100 million years. They are blue and hotter than the Sun. They burn rapidly and are already in middle age. Our Sun is also in its middle age, but it's burning much slower and is already four billion years old. The Crab Nebula, M1, is the remnant of a 1054 A.D. supernova. Binoculars 7X50 or larger barely reveal a dim, colorless oval. A telescope is required to see any details.

OBJECT	MAG	DESCRIPTION
M1	8.4	The Crab Nebula. Faint oval disk in binoculars.
M45	1.6	Seven visual stars. Dozens of stars in binoculars.

Orion

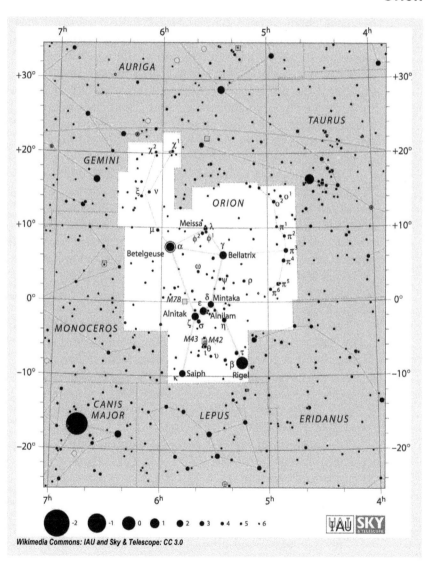

Wikimedia Commons: IAU and Sky & Telescope: CC 3.0

Orion is the most conspicuous and recognized constellation of the Heavens, with competition perhaps from the Big Dipper asterism of Ursa Major. In Greek mythology Orion was a strong and mighty hunter. Orion culminates at midnight in December. Canis Major, the faithful dog with the bright star Sirius, follows Orion's westward march. At the beginning of this chapter is an image of Orion from Johannes Hevelius's 17th-century star atlas. Old star atlases often depicted figures backward, as if viewed from Heaven beyond the constellation, looking back toward Earth. The bright star Betelgeuse is a shoulder, Rigel is a foot, Alnitak, Alnilam, and Mintaka are his belt. A sword hangs from his belt. The belt is near the celestial equator, so observers from the far north (85°N) to the far south (75°S) can view him. The great hunter stands on his head for southern viewers.

Orion rewards northern observers willing to brave Winter nights. Of course, there is M42, the emission nebula in the middle of Orion's sword that is naked-eye visible. In binoculars, it's clearly a nebula. A telescope reveals a large fan of nebulosity with color to the southwest separated by a dark nebula from M43 to the northeast. In the brightest part of M42 is the multiple star system called the Trapezium. The nebula and embedded Trapezium is perhaps the greatest telescopic wonder in the Heavens.

The brightest star that forms Orion's head is Meissa or λ Ori. But even to the naked eye, it's a triangle of stars. Meissa itself is a double resolved in amateur telescopes. Binoculars reveal this triangle of stars as an open cluster with over a dozen stars called Collinder 69. Per Collinder (1890 – 1974) was a Swedish astronomer who created a catalog of 471 open clusters in 1931.

The western star in Orion's belt, δ Ori or Mintaka, is an excellent binocular double with the visible primary and a magnitude six secondary. NGC1981, which resolves with binoculars into just over a half-dozen stars with light from unresolved stars, is just north of the sword's northernmost star. In binoculars, M78 is a small, dim nebulosity.

The Horsehead nebula requires at least an 8-inch telescope and a nebula filter to see. This wide-angle photograph shows Orion's three belt stars and the

Horsehead nebula, the small dark nebula on the nebula's bright edge just south of the belt star Alnitak. Photographs at higher magnification reveal a conspicuous horsehead. This photograph also shows some of the nebulosity in the entire Orion region present in long-exposure photos.

OBJECT	MAG	DESCRIPTION
M42	4.0	Naked eye visible. Perhaps the best emission nebula for binoculars.
M78	8.2	Looks like a dim comet with two stars in the head.
NGC1981	4.2	Binoculars reveal about 9 stars. Not on the chart. See text for location.

Auriga

Auriga is Latin for charioteer. Auriga culminates at midnight in December, north of Orion. The Winter Milky Way passes through Auriga.

Capella, a beautiful yellow star that is the third brightest in the northern celestial hemisphere, dominates Auriga. Capella is circumpolar for observers north of 44°N

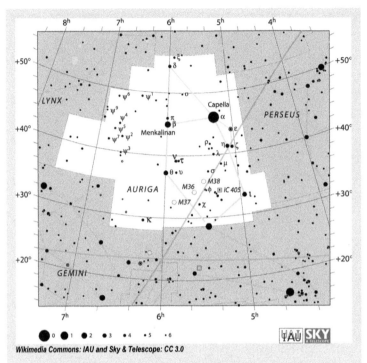

latitude. Capella is a four-star system. The two primary stars are a spectroscopic binary, meaning they were too close to resolve by telescopes, and in 1899 spectral line shifts revealed two stars orbiting about each other. By 1936, spectroscopic examination revealed a system with four stars.

Auriga is home to three Messier objects, all open clusters. In binoculars, M36 and M38 resolve into a few stars, with the unresolved stars providing a background glow. M37 is similar but a little more striking. IC405, the Flaming Star Nebula, requires a telescope to observe. The several stars labeled ψ Aur once formed the constellation Telescopium Herschelii established to honor Herschel's Uranus discovery. This constellation fell from use in the 19th century.

OBJECT	MAG	DESCRIPTION
M36	6.3	Open cluster with a few stars resolved in binoculars.
M37	6.2	This is perhaps the best of the three open clusters.
M38	7.4	Open cluster with a few stars resolved in binoculars.

The Southern Sky

Early astronomy development occurred primarily north of 30°N, and celestial catalogs initially lacked entries deep in the southern celestial hemisphere. The French astronomer Nicolas-Louis de Lacaille traveled to the Cape of Good Hope. From 1750 to 1754, he built an observatory near the southwestern coast and observed nearly 10,000 stars and nebulae. In 1763 he published his southern catalog *Coelum Australe Stelliferum* and named 14 constellations that are standard today. William Herschel's *Catalogue of Nebulae and Clusters of Stars* did not include deep southern entries. William's son, John Herschel, traveled to South Africa, added southern entries, and published a compiled catalog of his father's and his entries in 1864. John Louis Emil Dreyer's follow-up *New General Catalogue of Nebulae and Clusters of Stars* (NGC), followed by the supplemental *Index Catalogues* (IC), includes a comprehensive list of both northern and southern objects.

The southern-most object in the Messier catalog is M7, the Ptolemy Cluster, at declination -34.79°S. However, some of the best examples of both open and globular clusters and the most visible galaxies external to the Milky Way are located deep in southern skies.

This circular star chart is the sky south of declination 40°S. The south celestial pole is the center of the chart. The chart's perimeter includes the right ascension and the month that region culminates at midnight above the southern celestial pole. For example, the constellation Crux is at the highest elevation at midnight in early April. In October at midnight, Phoenix is at its highest elevation above the southern horizon.

Two Heavenly objects in southern skies are the Small Magellanic Cloud (SMC) and the Large Magellanic Cloud (LMC). They appear like small detached pieces of the Milky Way. They are irregular dwarf galaxies and are members of the local galaxy group that includes the Milky Way. Antonio Pigafetta (c. 1491 – 1531), an assistant to Ferdinand Magellan (1480 – 1521), described the clouds during the Earth's first circumnavigation.

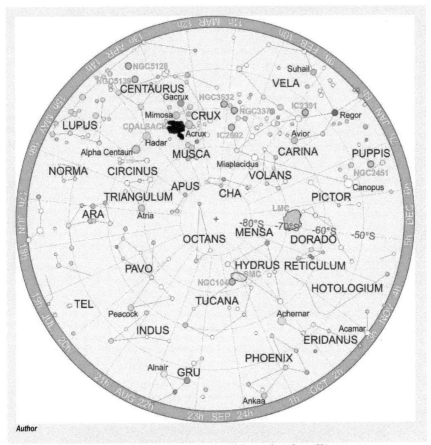

Author

The SMC includes several hundred million stars, nebulae, clusters, and HII regions. It's about 200,000 ly distant. The LMC was first written about by the Persian astronomer Al Sufi (903 – 986) in his *Book of Fixed Stars* in 964, calling it Al Bakr, the White Ox. The LMC is 163,000 ly distant. The SMC and LMC share a bridge of gas, suggesting a past interaction and gravitational connection.

NGC 104, also called 47 Tuc or ξ Tuc, is a magnificent naked-eye globular cluster with a total magnitude of 4.1. While its stars are unresolved in binoculars, it does appear rather large and bright. NGC2451 is a stunning open cluster that resolves into dozens of stars in binoculars. It's two open clusters along the same line of sight. The closer is at 600 ly and the more distant at 1,200 ly. Another stunning open cluster that is naked-eye visible is IC 2391 in Vela. Binoculars reveal two dozen stars. And yet another outstanding open cluster is IC 2602, also called the Southern Pleiades. Like its northern sister, its blue stars are beautiful in binoculars. It spans too much sky for telescopes except those with a wide-angle view.

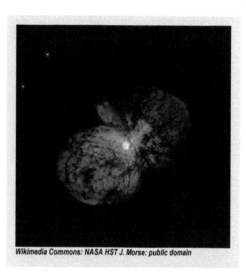

Wikimedia Commons: NASA HST J. Morse: public domain

Carina's Great Nebula, NGC 3372, is undoubtedly one of Heaven's most magnificent nebulae, considerably larger and brighter than the Great Orion Nebula. Naked-eye visible, it's a showpiece in binoculars. Dark lanes divide the nebula into multiple sections and individual open clusters. Telescopically it's a sight to behold. Within the Carina Nebula is the star η Car which in 1843 became the second brightest star in the sky. It faded rapidly and was below naked-eye visibility for a hundred years, beginning in the 1860s. It has brightened to magnitude 4.5. If you're looking for a candidate for the next supernova event in our galaxy, η Car is a good bet. The Great Nebula surrounds this star in this false-color image taken by the HST in the red and near-ultraviolet spectrum.

NGC 3532, the Pincushion Cluster, is a naked-eye, brilliant open cluster in Carina that John Herschel described as one of the finest star clusters in the sky. In binoculars, it erupts into a field of over 50 primarily hot-blue stars. It covers an area twice the size of the Moon.

Crux is Latin for cross. The Southern Cross is the smallest of all the constellations, but it lives big in the heart of those who see it. The flags of Australia, New Zealand, Brazil, Samoa, and Papua New Guinea feature the Southern Cross, easily recognized because the four stars forming the cross are bright. The brightest, Acrux, is magnitude 0.77, and the dimmest, δ Cru, is magnitude

Wikimedia Commons: ESO: CC 4.0

2.79. The Southern Cross lies on the meridian at the same time as the Big Dipper. Observers between latitudes 20°N and 25°S can see the Southern Cross and the Big Dipper simultaneously. When Crux is highest above the southern horizon, Ursa Major is highest above the northern horizon. That occurs around 4 am in January, midnight in March, and 9 pm in May.

A degree southeast of Mimosa, the second brightest star in Crux, is NGC 4755, the Jewel Box Nebula, which John Herschel described as *"...a superb piece of fancy jewellery."* Binoculars reveal a tight group of a few stars in the shape of an arrowhead. Just south of the Jewel Box is the Coalsack, a dense dark nebula obscuring the Milky Way background. The Coalsack is perhaps the finest hole in the Milky Way of all the visible dark nebulae.

We now come to the grandest globular cluster in all of the Heavens, Omega Centauri, or NGC 5139. It's the largest of all the globular clusters in the Milky Way, contains an estimated ten million stars, and is 15,800 ly distant. Like other globulars, it's ancient, almost as old as the universe. Like many galaxies, it may contain a massive black hole in its core.

Although described in this southern skies tour, Omega Centauri peaks above the southern horizon for observers as far north as latitude 40°N with a clear view of the horizon and ideal conditions. At magnitude 3.9, it's naked-eye visible. In very dark skies, its dimmest extremes make it appear as a large fuzzy star. In large binoculars, it has a grainy appearance, hinting that it's a ball of stars. The largest binoculars resolve a few stars. The view in my 24-inch telescope in New Mexico was memorable, to say the least.

I end the tour of southern gems with the peculiar galaxy NGC 5128, Centaurus A. It has a super-massive black hole at its center with a mass of 55 million Suns. In

Wikimedia Commons: ESO: CC 4.0

professional telescopes, jets of material extend broadside away from the galaxy above and below its plane. In this close-up image, dust lanes and red star-forming H II regions are visible. Centaurus A is a strong radio and X-ray emitter. At magnitude 6.8, it's not a naked-eye object, but binoculars reveal it isn't simply a star.

OBJECT	MAG	DESCRIPTION
NGC104	4.1	47 Tucanae. Second brightest globular in the Heavens.
IC2391	2.5	Binoculars reveal about two dozen stars, including doubles.
NGC2451	3.0	Binoculars reveal 30 or so stars, a red star surrounded by blue stars.
IC2602	1.9	Southern Pleiades. Bright cluster of 60 stars. Very far south.
NGC3372	1.0	Carina Nebula. Huge, absolutely stunning in binoculars.
NGC3532	3.0	Pincushion Cluster. Brilliant cluster with 60 stars in binoculars.
NGC4755	4.2	Jewel Box. A degree SE of Mimosa. Small but bright cluster.
NGC5128	6.8	Centaurus A, bizarre radio galaxy. Looks like a fuzzy star in binos.
NGC5139	3.9	Omega Centauri. Brightest globular in all of the Heavens. Stunning.

With perhaps one exception, the Milky Way is home to everything we can see in the Heavens with our naked eyes. For the first twenty-two years of my life, I lived in a tiny midwestern town without street lights, far from any large town. After that, as I lived in larger cities, my planned pilgrimages to dark skies were a welcomed chance to marvel at the night sky and the Milky Way. Life often comes full circle, and more recently, I'm blessed with dark skies again. A precious few of my earthly companions share this blessing.

But now, we'll leave our Milky Way home for the endless void beyond, a void from which so little light reaches us that only optical aid brings it into view. However, 400 years of improvements to telescopes now reveal Heavens of astronomical beauty. Turn the page.

9 Deep Space

We have explored the beautiful Milky Way, its stars, its nebulae, its constellations. As we venture outward millions and billions of light-years, we are not only traveling unimaginable distance, but we are traveling back in time. The photons that reach our eyes left their source long, long ago. The distance turns out to be a sort of way-back time machine. But those ancient photons bear an amazingly detailed story, and science continues to decode that story.

The Nebulae Mystery

Oh, the beautiful Milky Way. In Greek mythology, the god Hermes placed the infant Heracles at the breast of the sleeping queen of the gods, Hera. When she awoke, she tore the infant from her breast and spilled her milk across the Heavens. But in 1609, Galileo turned his telescope on the Milky Way and learned the Milky Way is composed of a myriad of stars. Roughly 300 years later, Edwin Hubble turned the newly completed giant Hooker telescope on Mt. Wilson on our neighbor galaxy, Andromeda. The result once again changed astronomy.

During the 19th century, as astronomers turned improved telescopes to the Heavens, catalogs grew to thousands of non-stellar objects. Many turned out to be clusters of stars, and others looked like clouds of gas. But most were oval or spiral patches of light. A debate raged on the nature of the nebulae, Latin for cloud or fog.

Laplace's 1796 theory about the formation of our solar system was popular during the 19th century. In his theory, stars form from collapsing, swirling clouds of gas. Perhaps these nebulae were solar systems forming throughout the

Milky Way. The discovery that many of the nebulae were spirals supported this idea. By the 1880s, telescopic photography revealed these nebulae were even more numerous than had been thought. The message was clear. Star formation was occurring everywhere in the galaxy. During this time, as more and more nebulae were recorded, a new development was advancing. Fraunhofer, written about in the first chapter, had discovered lines in the spectrum of light. Replacing the eye with a spectroscope at the telescope's focus revealed the elements that generated the light. In 1864, a wealthy British amateur astronomer William Huggins (1824 – 1910) turned his telescope on a nebula. Lo and behold, the spectrum was not the complex spectrum of a star but the single line of gas. Soon, astronomers everywhere were getting on board with the theory that the nebulae were gas clouds in the process of forming stars. William Huggins's choice of targets was unfortunate.

Wikimedia Commons: Daube aus Boblingen: public domain

IMMANUEL KANT
(1724 – 1804) Prussian philosopher

Immanuel Kant was an influential philosopher during the Enlightenment. He believed that things exist, but we only know them as they appear to us. His influence on philosophy remains to this day. He was neither an astronomer nor a scientist. Nevertheless, after reading and misinterpreting the summary of an erroneous astronomy book, Kant correctly imagined that the Milky Way was a vast swirling disk of stars and that the nebulae were similar but distant "island universes." Unfortunately, Kant's 1755 book on the subject, *Universal Natural History and Theory of the Heavens,* wasn't published before the publisher went bankrupt. However, the manuscript survived.

Huggins later studied the spectrum of the largest of all the nebulae, the Andromeda Nebula. It had a stellar spectrum! An assumption that one theory could explain all nebulae was one cause of the great mystery. But the Laplacian protostar hypothesis for the nebulae was too entrenched to die.

In 1908, Hale completed the 60-inch telescope on Mt. Wilson. Unlike stars, globular clusters are not confined to the Milky Ways disk but scatter in a vast spherical arrangement around the galaxy called the halo. In 1912, the discovery of a relationship between the period and the absolute luminosity of Cepheid variables provided an estimate of their distance. In 1917, an American scientist Harlow Shapley (1885 – 1972), working at Mt. Wilson, used Cepheid variables in globular clusters to determine their distance. Assuming the globulars are randomly scattered, the Milky Way center may be inferred once the distances to many are found. In a repeat of the ancient erroneous Earth-centric view, astronomers had previously assumed the Sun was near the galaxy center. Shapley showed that the center was far away in the direction of the constellation Sagittarius. He also determined the diameter of the galaxy was roughly 300,000 ly. Because he underestimated the extinction of light by galactic dust and errors in early models of Cepheids, his size estimate was three times the modern figure. Still, it was more accurate than previous estimates. The research established Shapley's renown.

In 1917, an influential telescope designer, George Ritchey (1864 - 1945), and an astronomer, Heber Curtis (1872 - 1942), found novae in old telescope photographic images of nebulae, which suggested that the nebulae are composed of stars.

The argument came to a head on April 26, 1920, at a debate sponsored by the National Academy of Science in Washington, DC. Shapley and Curtis debated the question. Science is ostensibly objective, but humans conduct it. Shapley felt compelled to defend "his" gigantic galaxy as the entire universe, which meant the nebulae were a part of the Milky Way. Curtis took the stance that the spiral nebulae were remote galaxies.

The debate did not settle the argument. By 1924, using the newer and even larger 100-inch Hooker telescope at Mt. Wilson, Edwin Hubble claimed to have photographed individual stars in the nebulae M31 and M33. Shapley dismissed the specks as mere curds in a Laplacian nebula. However, Shapley's defense of his Milky Way would not stand the test of time. Some of the nebulae in Shapley's Milky Way were indeed gas clouds, but the vast majority were island universes, just as Kant had surmised 165 years earlier.

Galaxy Types

All galaxies have at least two things in common: they are larger than other objects (except for collections of themselves), and they contain a vast number of stars. By the time the 100-inch Hooker reflector on Mt. Wilson was operational, an extensive collection of galactic images was available. In 1926, Edwin Hubble developed a morphological classification of galaxies based on their

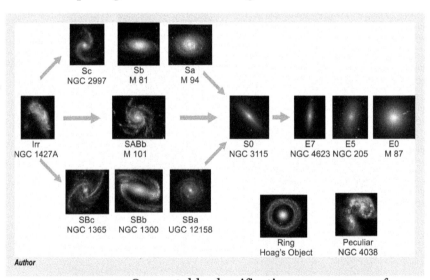

appearance. One notable classification was a group of galaxies that had no discernable spiral arms. They are called elliptical galaxies. Of the larger systems, about one-fifth of the galaxies fell into this category. Hubble classified them based on how elongated they appeared, with E0 being circular and E7 for the most elongated.

About 77% of the galaxies had spiral arms. Hubble subdivided the spiral galaxies into two categories: those with a central bar, SB, and those without, S. He classified the unbarred spirals from *a* to *c* depending on the tightness of the spiral arms, with Sc being open spirals and Sa tightly wound spirals. A similar system classified the tightness of barred spirals. Hubble based his classification on appearance. Because gas and dust obscure our view of the Milky Way, we can only reconstruct its form using multiple data sources. When I was in college, astronomers classified the Milky Way as Sb. Today, it's classified as SBb barred spiral. Hubble's classification scheme is also called his tuning-fork diagram because of its shape.

The remaining small percentage of galaxies are classified as irregular (Irr), ring(r), or peculiar (pec). These classifications are also used as suffixes. For example, a galaxy with spiral arms and a visible ring could be classified as Sb(r). The Small and Large Magellanic Clouds are irregular galaxies. A peculiar classification is used for galaxies that defy normal classification.

Genes that fix living organisms in more specific classes aid taxonomy classification in biology. Galaxy classification is a continuum and often subjective. For example, consider the case where a bar is so small as to be insignificant.

In 1959, the French-born astronomer Gerard de Vaucouleurs (1918 - 1995), working at the Harvard Observatory, revised the Hubble scheme to include ring, peculiar, and galaxies intermediate between normal and barred spirals. The intermediate class was labeled SAB. For example, Messier 101 is a SABb galaxy. A difficulty with both systems is that the nature of the arms in edge-on galaxies is hidden. Another difficulty is that tilt to our line of sight can obfuscate the actual elongation of elliptical galaxies. Many galaxies are unusual in some respects, and researchers sometimes create new subcategories. As a result, classifications are far from standardized. Nevertheless, astronomers still use the Hubble/de Vaucouleurs classification system.

The classic irregular galaxy has no central bulge, doesn't have pronounced arms, is smaller than other galaxies, and has a preponderance of young stars.

The So class is called a lenticular galaxy. They are intermediate between spiral and elliptical galaxies. Like spirals, they have a flattened disk and have a central bulge. Like ellipticals, they are void of arms and are composed primarily of old stars.

Ring galaxies are rare, comprising fewer than 1% of the galaxies. None of Messier's objects are ring galaxies. One of the most stunning examples is Hoag's Object, discovered in 1950 and pictured in the Hubble classification diagram. It's too dim for amateur telescopes. A small number of NGC objects have both rings and arms. The brightest of these is NGC1291, but it represents a classic case of the classification's subjective nature. One photograph may suggest a ring, and another suggests two arms far from the core.

Wikimedia Commons: NASA: public domain

Peculiar galaxies are more common. Somewhere around 5 to 10% of galaxies could be classified as peculiar. Peculiar galaxies often result from the interaction of two or more galaxies. An example is the Antennae Galaxies, NGC4038 and NGC4039. An active galactic nucleus, caused by a massive black hole at the core, also may result in peculiar forms. The black hole's accretion of surrounding material may cause radio, X-ray, and even visible distortions that classify the galaxy as peculiar. In 1966, the American astronomer Halton Arp (1927 – 2013) published the Atlas of Peculiar Galaxies, which contained photographs of peculiar galaxies, many of which resulted from galactic collisions. This catalog includes numerous objects within reach of amateur telescopes and even binoculars. By the way, Arp is one of the very few modern astronomers who never accepted the Big Bang theory, which we will take up later in this chapter.

The Local Group

The 18th-century term "island universes" for the galaxies is perhaps less descriptive than the modern term, archipelago universes. Galaxies often group together. There are clusters of galaxies and clusters of clusters called superclusters. The Milky Way is no exception. The Local Group is a cluster of some 80 or more galaxies dominated by the Milky Way and the Magellanic clouds in one area, and the Andromeda Galaxy and the Triangulum Galaxy in a second area. Scattered among these larger galaxies are many dwarf galaxies.

Hubble coined the term Local Group in his 1936 book, *The Realm of the Nebulae.* He placed twelve objects in the Local Group, as shown in the table. The masses given in the table are in solar masses and are approximate. In recent years they have changed significantly.

Also, the quantity of objects in the local group

OBJECT	MASS	DIST(ly)	MAG
Milky Way	1.0×10^{12}		
Andromeda	1.5×10^{12}	2,500,000	3.44
Triangulum	5×10^{10}	2,730,000	5.7
LMC	1×10^{10}	163,000	0.9
SMC	7×10^{9}	200,000	2.7
M 32	3×10^{9}	2,600,000	8.1
M 110	9.3×10^{9}	2,700,000	8.9
NGC 6822	1.3×10^{8}	1,600,000	9.3
IC 1613	1×10^{8}	2,400,000	9.9
NGC 147	?	2,500,000	10.5
NGC 185	?	2,000,000	10.1
IC 10	?	2,200,000	10.4

increased over time. By 2003 the count had reached 36. The current count of 80 doesn't include other potential members that are obscured from view by the dark clouds of the Milky Way. Many of the recently discovered members are very dim and were not found photographically, but by reducing data gathered by automated telescopes cataloging millions of stars.

Observing Galaxies

The photons that traveled millions of years from the galaxies to reach us are not tired. They arrive with the same energy they left home with. They once were uncountable, but they spread over a sphere of unimaginable radius. The inverse square law dwindled them to almost none. Our eyes gather them up through irises of 1/5-inch diameter. Binoculars gather them from 2-inch pieces of glass, so there are 100 times more photons. An 8-inch amateur telescope gathers 1600 times as many as the eye. The five behemoth modern telescopes have mirrors that collect 4,000,000 times as many photons. But bigger telescopes represent only a part of the progress. Beginning in the late 1800s, photographic film at the focus of telescopes piled up photons over long exposures. Today, digital cameras turn photons into electrons with high efficiency. By the way, your eyes do the same thing. Your retina converts the photons that pass through your iris into electrons that the optic nerves transfer to your brain. Digital camera images from multiple nights are stacked in computers to gather even more photons. The result is stunning photos of the distant galaxies. Pictured here is the Triangulum Galaxy, a member of our local group, taken by the HST.

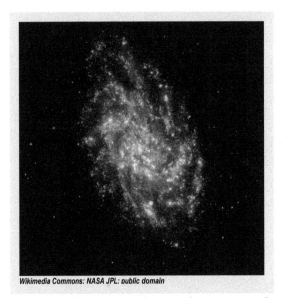

Wikimedia Commons: NASA JPL: public domain

When you look through binoculars or even a telescope, these latest advances are missing. The result is a disappointing, fuzzy, dim, featureless, colorless patch of light. But amateur astronomers peer through their telescope night after night while freezing in the Winter and swatting mosquitoes in summer. Why? For me, it's a combination of wonder and understanding what I see. Each faint glow is as many as a billion stars, many perhaps circled by planets with civilizations: empires that wax and wane and fields of flowers that bloom and fade.

As I peer at the Andromeda galaxy, perhaps Princess Andromeda is looking back. Maybe her father, King Cepheus, built for her a giant telescope mirror the diameter of 50,000 Earth solar orbits, fashioned with a figure accurate to 2 millionths of an inch. Then Andromeda could watch the wanderings of Earthlings. But alas, as she watches us, we have been gone millions of years. Technology will never create that mirror. But the Creator already has, in the mind of your author. Each fuzzy patch of light I see in my modest telescope is a beacon from the creation. Amateur astronomers seek to grasp the creation by observing just one more dim patch of light.

Images from the HST suggest there are approximately 100 billion galaxies. As telescope technology continues to advance, the number will undoubtedly rise. The Herschel catalog contains 2514 celestial objects discovered long ago using primarily his 6.2, 12, and 18.7-inch reflectors. Many are galaxies. The Messier catalog includes 40 galaxies, all of which are visible in amateur telescopes and some with binoculars.

Moonless skies away from city lights are a must for viewing galaxies. The magnitude of extended objects like galaxies and nebulae can be deceiving. The larger an area the light is spread over, the dimmer the object appears to be. Astronomers refer to the brightness of extended objects as surface brightness. For example, the Triangulum Galaxy has a total magnitude of 5.7, but the light spreads over a large size. It's a very challenging target, even with binoculars. In the following table are my four favorite galaxies to observe with binoculars or small telescopes.

Andromeda, M31, can barely be seen with the naked eye. In binoculars, it's a beautiful sight that appears several times larger than the Moon. The outer fringes are dim, but it brightens noticeably toward the core. It's similar in size to the Milky Way and a member of the local group. Light has traveled only 2.5 million years to reach us, so it's close.

GALAXY	CONST	SIZE (min)	MAG
Andromeda M31/M32/M110	Andromeda	190 X 60	3.44
Whirlpool M51	Canes Venatici	11X7	8.4
Leo Triplet M66/M65/NGC3628	Leo	9 X 4	8.9
Bode's/Cigar M81/M82	Ursa Major	27 X 14 / 11 X 4	6.9/8.4

The Andromeda section of the chapter Constellations describes how to find it. In the same field of view, you should see a satellite galaxy of Andromeda, M32. It's a bright spot just south of the core. With very large binoculars, or better still a telescope, a third galaxy, M110, is barely visible northwest of the core. M110 is larger but dimmer than M32.

The Whirlpool Galaxy is in the constellation Canes Venatici. Latin for hunting dogs, Canes Venatici offers few bright stars to recognize. The constellation is due south of the three bright stars forming the handle of the Big Dipper. The brightest star, Cor Caroli, is in the middle of the constellation shining at only magnitude 2.9. Although Canes Venatici has no bright stars, it's home to several galaxies and Messier objects. The most remarkable of the galaxies is the Whirlpool which can be found by sweeping

3.5° southwest of Alkaid, the bright star at the dipper handle's end.

Binoculars reveal a small circular patch of light that is brighter toward the center. Binoculars will not show the satellite galaxy NGC5195, nor the spiral arms that are so clearly visible in this HST image. The first to see the spiral arms was the Anglo-Irish astronomer, William Parsons (1800 – 1867), using his "Leviathan of Parsontown" reflector, the largest in the world until the 100-inch Hooker at Mt. Wilson was completed in 1917. It requires about 8-inches of aperture to see NGC5195 clearly, and about 12-inches to see detail in the spiral arms.

The Leo Triplet is a group of three galaxies just south of the triangular-shaped hindquarters of Leo. In this image, M66 is near the bottom, M65 is to the upper right, and NGC 3628 is to the upper left. The brightest star at the center top is about

Wikimedia Commons: Anttler: CC 3.0

magnitude seven and is relatively bright in binoculars. The finder chart for the constellation Leo may be used to locate M66 and M65. Both M65 and M66 are visible as dim oval patches of light in binoculars. M65 appears more edge-on than M66. The edge-on NGC3628 with prominent dust lanes in this photograph is beyond the reach of any but the largest binoculars.

Bode's Galaxy, M81, and the Cigar Galaxy, M82, are a pair of galaxies separated by just over 0.5°. Bode's Galaxy is class SAab and has a supermassive black hole in its core. M82 classifies as a starburst galaxy. It's generating new stars in the center of the galaxy at a rate nearly ten times that of the entire Milky Way. M81 and

Wikimedia Commons: Anttler: CC 3.0

M82 make a striking pair in one field of view in binoculars. They can be located using the star chart of Ursa Major. M81 is the brighter of the two and appears as an oval haze in binoculars. M82 is a magnitude and a half dimmer but viewed edge-on, its smaller area increases the surface brightest, and the difference in brightness is not as pronounced as might be expected.

Hubble Extremely Deep Field

If a beautiful image of a galaxy holding a billion stars is awe-inspiring, imagine a photo holding 5,000 galaxies. The HST launched into low-Earth orbit in 1990. The mirror's figure was flawed, but some science was possible. Three years later, after a repair mission installed corrective optics, the HST achieved its design objectives.

The HST supports different observation styles. In 1995, astronomers decided to image a small section of the sky as deep into space as possible. The sky area would need to be small because the field of view for such a powerful telescope is narrow, approximately 0.043°. That is the angle subtended by a grain of sand held at arm's length. It takes 24,000,000 fields that size to cover the sky. The chosen field needed to be free of bright stars that would overwhelm the camera with photons. The Earth or Moon should not occult the field, and it should be in a direction so that Earth-based optical and radio telescopes could perform follow-up observations. The first field chosen was near the Big Dipper. Many images would be taken and stacked by computer. This first effort was called the Hubble Deep Field, and the image was released in 1996. The program was so successful that a second field was imaged in 1998 in the southern skies in the constellation Tucana.

In 2002, another HST service mission installed an improved HST imaging system called the Advanced Camera for Surveys. That year, planning began for an even deeper reach into space called the Hubble Ultra-Deep Field. A second camera on the HST and additional

Wikimedia Commons: NASA HST: public domain

exposure time resulted in the release in 2009 of the Hubble Ultra-Deep Field.

The deepest field, the Hubble eXtreme Deep Field, was released in 2012. It involved the combination of 2 million seconds of exposure time. Very few of the objects in this image are stars in our galaxy. There are some 5,500 galaxies in this image, and the oldest is approximately 13.2 billion years old, very near the beginning of time.

Einstein Rings

Light travels in a straight line. Einstein's General Theory of Relativity predicts that gravity bends light. Actually, the theory predicts that gravity warps space. So light travels in a straight line through curved space. Arthur Eddington proved the theory correct in 1919 by observing bent starlight during a solar eclipse.

Many deep space photos reveal the bending of light by a massive object in front of a background object resulting in the distortion of the background object into an arc of light. In this image, a large red galaxy with a mass about ten times that of the Milky Way is precisely in front of a bluer background galaxy. The red galaxy is LRG3-757, discovered and cataloged by the automated telescopic Sloan Digital Sky Survey in 2007. This image is a follow-up photograph by the HST. The ring is multiple, distorted versions of the bluer galaxy. The ring characteristics result from a combination of the mass distribution in the lensing galaxy and the lensed galaxy's shape. Examples with alignment precise enough for a nearly complete ring are rare. These are more than just pretty happenstances. Even partial rings allow the calculation of the mass of the foreground object.

When Worlds Collide

I hate to be an alarmist, but the Milky Way will collide with the Andromeda Galaxy. The Andromeda Galaxy is approaching us at a speed of about 245,000 miles per hour. It will take about 6.5 billion years for it to get here. But as Andromeda gets closer, the attraction will increase, and so will also the rate. Until 2012, astronomers didn't understand how fast it moves laterally (sideways). Scientists using Hubble data concluded Andromeda wasn't moving laterally fast enough to miss us. It looks like the year will be 4,500,002,020 AD, give or take a few million years. The Milky Way is moving through space as well. We observe the Andromeda Galaxy motion relative to ours.

So, what will happen during the collision? First of all, there won't be any collisions. At least they would be very, very rare. If our Sun were the size of a ping-pong ball, the size of the nearest star, Proxima Centauri, would be the size of a pea. The distance between the ping-pong ball and the pea would be 680 miles. As you can see, the random chance for collision is almost nonexistent. The two galaxies will pass right through each other.

Well, not quite. The effect of gravity with all this mass whizzing by is profound. Gravitational forces will fling stars, dust, and gas from the galaxies, and pressure waves will launch the birth of millions of new stars. Material from the Oort cloud surrounding the solar system will be knocked out of orbit and come raining down on us, pock-marking the Earth like the Moon. And those beautiful spiral arms will be all messed up, if not completely erased in the new Milkomeda.

How can we be so sure what will happen? First of all, interactions are not all that rare. There are 100 billion galaxies within reach of Hubble's eye. Earth-based telescope and Hubble images are full of example interactions. Light travels longer from more distant galaxies, so the images are also a giant time machine. There are images of galaxies about to interact, interacting galaxies, and galaxies that interacted long ago.

By the way, 4.5 billion years is also the current scientific estimate of when the Sun will run out of gas. Don't say I didn't give you an adequate warning.

Cepheids

Henrietta Swan Leavitt (1868 – 1921) was an astronomer at the turn-of-the-century, influential Harvard College Observatory. A graduate of Ratcliff College, she was hired to examine images on photographic plates to measure and catalog the brightness of stars. At the time, women were not allowed to operate telescopes, and she had taken only one class in astronomy. For a while, she left the observatory, traveled in Europe, returned to the US, and was an art assistant at Beloit College in Wisconsin. She returned to the Harvard Observatory in 1903, and being

Wikimedia Commons: Weber State Univ.: public domain
HENTRIETTA SWAN LEAVITT
(1868 – 1921) American
astronomer and "computer"

financially independent, she initially worked for free. Later she was paid $0.30 an hour.

The observatory director tasked her to study variable stars in the Small and Large Magellanic Clouds on photographic plates from the Harvard Boyden Station in Arequipa, Peru. She cataloged 1777 variable stars and noticed the brighter variables had a longer period of variability. In 1912, she published a paper in the director's and her name concerning that discovery. The article clearly stated the work was by Leavitt.

Figure 2 in that paper included the apparent magnitude plotted versus the logarithm of the period in days. The top plot is at magnitude maximum, and the bottom plot is at magnitude minimum. In the paper, Leavitt stated, "*A straight line can be readily drawn among each of the two series of points corresponding to maxima and minima, thus showing that there is a simple relation between the brightness of the Cepheid variables and their periods.*"

The consequence was clear. The pulsation period of a

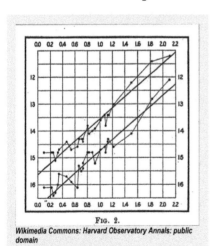

FIG. 2.
Wikimedia Commons: Harvard Observatory Annals: public domain

Cepheid reveals its absolute magnitude. Then, its apparent magnitude, as dimmed by distance, indicates the Cepheid's distance. The distance to one example Cepheid would calibrate the scale. A few years later, a parallax measurement found the distance to a Cepheid. Henrietta Leavitt wasn't allowed to operate her observatory's telescope, but her discovery remains today the measuring stick (called the standard candle) of the universe.

Expanding Universe

Chapter one described that the light emitted by an element contains lines of various intensity and spacing that serve as each element's fingerprint. If the source of that light is moving toward or away from us, the lines shift in frequency and reveal the source's velocity, in an effect called Doppler shift. If the light source moves away from us, the light shifts lower in frequency toward the red.

In 1912, the American astronomer Vesto Slipher (1875 – 1969) noted a blueshift in the Andromeda Galaxy spectrum. In 1915, Slipher reported on the shifts of 15 galaxies and noted that all but 3 were redshifted. By 1917, he had measured 25 galaxies, and 21 were redshifted. Because the galaxies' distances were unknown, astronomers didn't infer expansion.

During the 1920s, The Russian physicist and mathematician Arthur Friedman (1888 – 1925) and the Belgian priest, mathematician, and physicist Georges Lemaitre (1894 – 1966) wrote (despite Einstein's skepticism) that the General Theory of Relativity predicts the expansion of the universe.

Einstein was disturbed that the theory predicted the universe must either expand or contract. Because of his philosophical distaste for an expanding universe, Einstein introduced a term called the cosmological constant to his theory so that expansion was unnecessary.

While this theoretical work was happening in Europe, at the 100-inch Hooker telescope at Mt. Wilson, Edwin Hubble and an assistant, Milton Humason, were steadily measuring the Doppler shift in more and more galaxies, along with their distance using Leavitt's Cepheid standard candle. Hubble released results for 46 galaxies. He showed that the farther a galaxy was from us, the faster it was receding from us. If all of space is expanding, this relationship would exist from any viewpoint. Early measurements by Slipher were of closer galaxies. While a river moves unceasingly to the sea, local eddies may cause water in places to move upstream.

Wikimedia Commons: Huntington Digital Library: public domain

EDWIN POWELL HUBBLE
(1889 – 1953) American astronomer

Ironically, as late as 1941, Hubble was still skeptical that the redshift was due to an expanding universe. He insisted on using the term "apparent" velocity for the receding galaxies. One problem he couldn't resolve was that working the numbers backward gave an age of the universe of only 2 billion years.

By working at the same Hooker telescope Hubble had used, the German-born American astronomer Walter Baade (1893 – 1960) resolved the dilemma. Taking advantage of World War II blackouts in nearby Los Angeles, Baade discovered two classes of stars: early Population II stars born from the initial low-metal universe and older Population I stars born after metal enrichment. Cepheids exist in both populations but with different luminosity/period relations. Baade announced this discovery to the amazement of the 1952 meeting of the International Astronomical Union. Once taken into account, Hubble's universe grew by a factor of two. That still wasn't quite big enough. Over the decades, additional observations and refinements further increased the age of the expanding universe.

Remember Paul Dirac's admonition that beauty is more important than the theory fitting all the data. Be patient, and the data will one day fit a beautiful theory. Einstein's original theory predicted an expanding universe, but at the time, available data suggested the universe was not expanding. Einstein added the cosmological constant so the universe could be static. He later remarked his "biggest blunder" was adding the cosmological constant to make the data of the time fit his theory. Einstein realized he should have been patient.

The Big Bang

Today, the Big Bang theory prevails among cosmologists as the model explaining the universe as a whole. This was not always so. Until the 1960s, a strong competitor of the Big Bang theory was the Steady State theory which asserted that the expanding universe continuously creates matter, thus filling voids caused by expansion. The universe wasn't created but had always existed as it is now.

The Big Bang existed as a theory before Fred Hoyle inadvertently coined the name. In a 1949 BBC talk-show broadcast, Hoyle derisively stated, "these theories were based on the hypothesis that all the matter in the universe was created in one big bang at a particular time in the remote past." Hoyle was a prolific popular science and science fiction writer of the period, and he was a prominent astrophysicist with essential contributions to the theory of stellar fusion. Ironically, although Hoyle coined the term Big Bang, he was a proponent of the competing Steady State model. Over time, the Steady State theory lost favor simply because the Big Bang better explained more and more new observations.

Since the universe is expanding with time, traveling backward in time would shrink the universe. This idea naturally leads to a past time when all the universe's matter was crammed into an ultra-dense primeval atom, as Lamaitre called it. Particle physics today is a marriage of highly sophisticated quantum-theory mathematicians and experimental physicists testing those theories by smashing matter together at relativistic speeds. It turns out the union is getting along pretty well. Scientists believe they understand matter adequately to describe this primeval soup even before it consisted of atoms, as far back as tiny fractions of a second after the Big Bang. Here are the primary features of the current Big Bang theory.

The universe is expanding. The rate of expansion is called the Hubble constant. The velocity that galaxies recede from us increases with their distance from us. The units of the constant are kilometers per second divided by the distance in megaparsecs. Hubble originally placed the constant at 500. By 1958 it was estimated to be 75. Since 2007, many researchers using different independent techniques have valued the constant between 68 and 77.

The universe began at a specific time. The units of distance in the Hubble constant cancel, and the remaining factor is the inverse of time. That means the inverse of the Hubble constant is time. It's the age of the universe which is approximately 13.8 billion years.

The universe is big. Recall that the light from objects receding from us is redshifted. Objects traveling at the speed of light redshift to invisibility. As of 2020, the object with the greatest redshift is the galaxy GN-z11 at a distance of 13.39 billion ly. This measurement was taken using the HST and is another confirmation of the known universe's approximate age.

The universe is empty. All the stars we see with unaided eyes are stars within the Milky Way. Let's play a little mind game. It's a long way between galaxies. Suppose we were to drop out of warp drive at some random location in the universe. Because galaxies are far apart, a place selected at random is unlikely to be within a galaxy. So, what would we see? Probably nothing. Perhaps a dim fuzzy patch of light or two from distant galaxies, and they might almost be too faint to see like the Andromeda galaxy. The universe is mostly empty space, with an unimaginably low density of hydrogen and helium atoms here and there.

The ultimate fate of the universe is uncertain. The universe is expanding against the force of gravity which attempts to pull it back. If the universe's mass is sufficient, the expansion will ultimately halt and begin a collapse to the Big Crunch. If the mass is insufficient, the expansion will continue forever. If the mass is precisely critical, the expansion will continue but stop in infinite time. The current estimate of the mass of the universe is suspiciously close to critical. However, more recent discoveries suggest the expansion is accelerating. More about this later. In the meantime, science still has mysteries to pursue.

If the Big Bang sounds like some kind of big fireworks with matter exploding into space, it isn't. Instead, space itself is expanding, and the matter is along for the ride. Furthermore, there is no center like that of an exploding skyrocket. Although space appears to be three-dimensional, perhaps the best way to imagine a centerless universe is to consider the closed, two-dimensional surface of a balloon with spots. As the balloon expands, the dots on its surface spread apart. There is no center of the expansion. The expansion appears the same from all dots.

Let There Be Light

Here's the currently understood chronology of the Big Bang. Let's imagine at *time=0* God said, *"let time begin."* Soon after that, space expands by a huge factor in an infinitesimal fraction of a second. There are still no atoms, not even protons, neutrons, and electrons. This time is called the inflationary period, or cosmic inflation. Then the expansion rate slows to the current value. Somewhere around one second, quarks have bound together as protons and neutrons. Within a few minutes, the nucleus of atoms forms, but the small universe is still too hot for electrons to bind to nuclei. During this time, the universe is cooling rapidly. Over the next 370,000 years, the temperature falls from a billion degrees Kelvin to 4,000°K. The universe is an opaque soup of free nuclei and electrons.

Electrons begin binding to nuclei, and atoms form. This period is referred to as recombination, and it continues for 100,000 years. The universe becomes transparent, allowing photons of light to travel through space. But there are no photons because there are no stars, no sources of visible light in what is called the dark ages. God said, *"let there be light,"* and after hundreds of millions of years, the stars formed, and they continue forming, living, and dying to this day.

In 1948, two American cosmologists predicted photons from the recombination epoch would have cooled to about 5°K. Astronomers at the time missed the significance of this prediction. By the early 1960s, three Soviet physicists and independently an American astronomer Robert Dicke

Wikimedia Commons: NASA Bammesk: public domain

(1916 – 1997) resurrected the idea. Two colleagues of Dicke
began constructing equipment to detect this left-over heat
called the Cosmic Microwave Background (CMB). Before
Dicke's colleagues succeeded, Arno Penzias (1933 –
present) and Robert Wilson (1936 – present) working at
Bell Labs discovered the CMB in 1964. They were
investigating bouncing radio waves off a 100-foot and a
135-foot diameter Echo balloon satellites used for
communications purposes. Penzias and Wilson weren't
even looking for the CMB, but Dicke's colleagues only a few
miles away were preparing a search when they learned of
the Penzias and Wilson discovery. Penzias and Wilson
accidentally discovered the embers of the Big Bang. In this
photograph, Penzias and Wilson are standing beside the
large horn antenna used in their discovery. The CMB, a
predicted result of the Big Bang, convinced most
astronomers of the Big Bang model's superiority over the
Steady State model. Penzias and Wilson won the Nobel
Prize for their "accidental" discovery.

Resistance to the Big Bang

Initially, there was considerable resistance to the Big Bang model for not only scientific reasons but for religious reasons as well. This resistance kept the Steady State model afloat longer than was prudent. Science hates discontinuities and singularities. Quantum theory states an electron can orbit the nucleus at certain levels only. When an electron jumps from one level to another, it emits a photon of light. Strangely, the electron is never between levels, but it disappears from one level and is instantly at the next. This is a discontinuity. It doesn't make sense, and scientific principles abhor this behavior, leading to initial resistance to quantum theory, but quantum theory is now an important pillar of cosmology.

For some scientists, the resistance to the Big Bang was religious. Science has been a powerful force, the most potent force in history, for understanding the material world. Consequently, some scientists worship it with a religious faith that science will find a theory of everything given adequate time and effort. Like any religion practiced by humans, science isn't always tolerant.

The idea that at *time=0* there was nothing, and an instant later, there was an embryonic universe, was appalling to science. Even more appalling was the idea that science could never break through that moment in time. The other side of *time=0* is unknowable and embarrassingly inaccessible to science.

Einstein once wrote, *"This circumstance [of an expanding universe] irritates me,"* but later in life, he told a visitor he accepted *"a beginning."* Sir Arthur Eddington, who first proposed the Sun's energy source was fusion, wrote, *"the notion of a beginning is repugnant to me...I simply do not believe that the present order of things started off with a bang...it is preposterous..."* MIT physics professor Phillip Morrison (1915 – 2005) said, *"I find it hard to accept the Big Bang theory, I would like to reject it."* Allan Sandage (1926 – 2010), who followed in Hubble's footsteps at Mt. Wilson, said, *"It is such a strange conclusion...it cannot be true."*

The American astronomer Robert Jastrow (1925 –
2008) wrote in his book *God and the Astronomers:*

"It is not a matter of another year, another decade
of work, another measurement, or another theory;
at this moment it seems as though science will
never be able to raise the curtain on the mystery of
creation. For the scientist who has lived by his
faith in the power of reason, the story ends like a
bad dream. He has scaled the mountains of
ignorance; he is about to conquer the highest peak;
as he pulls himself over the final rock, he is greeted
by a band of theologians who have been sitting
there for centuries."

Dark Matter

The big and the little question in physics and
cosmology today is dark matter. It's big because
astronomers are searching the entire universe for it, and
it's little because particle physicists are also searching for
it. So, what is dark matter? The short answer is, there is no
answer. Not yet anyway. Although many astronomers and
particle physicists are looking, they don't know what
they're looking for.

Even though Einstein fixed Newton's laws for
relativistic speeds, Newton's laws are accurate at normal
speeds. Using Newton's laws, a high-school physics student
can describe how the Moon orbits the Earth, and NASA can
land a probe on Mars. The astronomer Fritz Zwicky (1898 -
1974) was born in Bulgaria to a Swiss father. He
immigrated to the United States in 1925 to work at the
California Institute of Technology. He was also on staff at
Mt. Wilson, and in 1933 he discovered an anomaly in the
rotational velocities of a cluster of galaxies in the
constellation Coma Berenices. He calculated the galaxies'
mass based on their rotational velocity around each other
and found the mass to be significantly more than expected
from their luminosity. He assumed the presence of
invisible mass and called it "dunkle materie," dark matter.

We accept the existence of things we can't see, like air, so his discovery didn't attract much attention.

In the 1970s, astronomer Vera Rubin measured the rotational velocity of stars in our neighbor, the Andromeda galaxy. She also concluded the presence of missing matter. Lots of it, in fact, about four-fifths of the matter seemed to be missing. This troubled astronomers who thought they understood galaxies and matter better than that. Rubin's seminal discovery redirected astronomical research, but decades later, the true nature of dark matter remains unknown.

Many forms of matter are invisible to telescopes. Black holes are one example. Dust and molecular hydrogen clouds are other examples. Brown dwarf "stars" are objects with insufficient mass for nuclear fusion to occur. Objects with a mass less than 0.07 to 0.09 solar masses never initiate substantial fusion. Given that slightly more massive light-emitting stars are the most numerous known stars, brown dwarfs are probably very common.

Normal matter, consisting of protons, neutrons, electrons, and a smattering of other particles, is referred to as baryonic matter. All known matter is this type, including the unseen examples just described. Many physicists and cosmologists believe that there isn't enough unseen baryonic matter to account for the missing matter. Some of the black holes and brown dwarfs would be aligned with background objects and cause lensing. Automated surveys have just not seen enough lensed objects to support that much regular unseen matter.

So, many scientists conclude that mysterious, non-baryonic matter exists. However, theoretical physicists have not identified a compelling candidate, and decades of searching by experimental physicists using particle accelerators, and other major detection projects, have failed. Scientists are becoming uneasy, and alternative theories are popping up. One of these is Modified Newton Dynamics or MOND. This theory posits that as the distance from the center of mass increases and gravity becomes weaker, gravity decreases linearly with distance rather than with distance squared, as Newton predicted. However, none of these alternative theories seem to match observations quite as well as dark matter.

To confound matters even worse, in 1998 and 1999, teams of astronomers observing supernovae in distant galaxies concluded the rate of expansion of the universe is increasing. The three discoverers of this increasing expansion received a 2011 Nobel Prize. The term dark energy was coined in 1998 to name the cause of this phenomenon. The nature of dark energy is also unknown.

According to NASA's data from the Wilkinson Microwave Anisotropy Probe, normal baryonic matter makes up 4.6% of the universe, dark matter is 24%, and dark energy is 71.4%. That's pretty precise data, considering we don't even know what two of them are. It seems to me the whole mess is pretty ugly. I wish for a more beautiful theory.

So, who cares? Does it really matter? Heinrich Hertz (1857-1894) proved the existence of radio waves in the 1880s. When asked about the ramification of his discovery, he replied, "nothing, I guess." Galaxies spinning too fast may not affect our personal lives, but what makes them do so just might. Besides, we all love a good mystery. Speaking of mysteries, up next is a mystery everyone talks about.

10 Aliens

"Do you think we are alone in the universe?" When asked this question by a child in the 1997 movie Contact, Jodie Foster playing Dr. Ellie Arroway responded, *"The universe is a pretty big place. Bigger than anyone has ever imagined. If we are, it's an awful waste of space."*

The Two Answers

Our Sun is nothing more than a typical star. There are billions of stars in our Milky Way galaxy and billions of galaxies in our observable universe. The quantity of stars is a number followed by so many zeros the human mind can't comprehend its reality. Whether there is or isn't life on other planets, there is certainly an opportunity.

Fermi's paradox espouses a different view. Enrico Fermi (1901 – 1954), an Italian physicist who immigrated to the US and was instrumental in developing nuclear fission for atomic power, posed a critical question. The universe is old. Some civilizations would be far older than ours and highly advanced. They would have developed interstellar travel long ago. If so, where are they? He concluded we are alone.

UFOs

Of course, some believe we have been visited. Perhaps Adam and Eve were dropped off with a suitcase full of fig leaves. Or maybe aliens helped build the pyramids.

Seriously, UFOs are a serious business. In 1561, Nuremberg residents of Nuremberg, Germany, observed a large black triangular object and hundreds of spheres, cylinders, and other objects flying erratically overhead. And it was April, not Octoberfest. Reports of strange flying objects continued throughout history. On June 24, 1947, a civilian pilot named Kenneth Arnold reported nine objects flying in formation in a saucer-like manner near Mt. Rainer, Washington. He reported the disks flying over 1,200 mph (or 1,000 mph, depending on the source). After that, the term "flying saucer" became popular, and large numbers of sightings began occurring in the US. This amateur photograph of a flying saucer was taken July 31, 1952, in Passaic, New Jersey.

In 1953, Captain Edward J. Ruppelt with the US Air

Wikimedia Commons: George Stock: public domain

Force coined the term Unidentified Flying Object (UFO). Ruppelt felt flying saucer or flying disk was misleading because the official mandate was to investigate *"any airborne object which by performance, aerodynamic characteristics, or unusual features, does not conform to any presently known aircraft or missile type, or which cannot be positively identified as a familiar object."*

The USAF conducted ongoing investigations from 1947 to 1969 under evolving program names including Project Sign, Project Grudge, and Project Blue Book. While various US government agencies today gather news and data on just about everything that happens worldwide, overt US government programs ended with the government scientist Edward Condon's report that further UFO programs were unjustifiable. The report mirrored previous government reports that sightings were primarily known objects, and most of the unsolved sightings were due to a lack of detailed or objective information. The National Academy of Scientists shared this conclusion. However, a subcommittee of the American Institute of Aeronautics and Astronautics thought the government should fund additional programs.

The government studies concluded that natural phenomena are the source of many UFO citings, including meteors, planets, bright stars, and saucer-shaped lenticular clouds. There are also manmade objects such as airplanes in unusual flight paths, weather balloons, and unusually high reconnaissance aircraft such as the U2. Pictured here is a photograph of a Fata Morgana mirage

Wikimedia Commons: Timpaananen: CC 3.0

that causes objects below the horizon to appear as though they are floating above the sea. Notice the larger boat is symmetrical and includes an inverted image superimposed beneath the top image. The photo also shows a smaller UFO to the right of the larger one. Despite government denial of UFOs, a desire to believe we are not alone, combined with a distrust of government agencies, keeps the idea alive.

Private UFO investigators referred to themselves as ufologists, and they have formed multiple organizations, including the Center for UFO Studies (CUFOS), the Mutual UFO Network (MUFON), the International UFO Congress, and the National UFO Reporting Center (NUFORC). The NUFORC website allows you to report citings or abductions and to view previous reports. There are thousands of them.

In the 1951 movie, *The Day the Earth Stood Still*, a UFO landed in Washington, D.C. In this day of omnipresent cell phone cameras, even clandestine landings would be hard to hide. I'm inclined to discount UFO reports. Besides, no better than we Earthlings get along with each other it might get a little hairy if aliens show up. Maybe civilizations were separated by vast distances for a reason.

The Drake Equation

Wikimedia Commons: R. Perrino: CC 2.0
DR. FRANK DRAKE
(1930 - present) American astronomer

While the idea of searching for little green men running through the woods is met with skepticism, searching for life out there somewhere is more credible. The American astronomer Frank Drake (1930 – present) worked at the National Radio Astronomy Observatory (NRAO) in Green Bank, West Virginia, and later the Jet Propulsion Laboratory in Pasadena. In 1961, Drake hosted a small meeting of ten scientists at NRAO, including a young Carl Sagan and three Nobel laureates to consider the Search for Extraterrestrial Intelligence (SETI). To prepare an agenda for the meeting, Drake developed what became known as the Drake equation:

$$N = R_s f_p N_e f_l f_i f_c L.$$

N is the quantity of civilizations in our galaxy with which communication is possible. R_s is the annual rate of star formation in the Milky Way, f_p is the fraction of stars with planets, N_e is the average number of those planets with an ecosystem, f_l is the fraction of those planets that develop life, f_i is the fraction of those that develop intelligent life, f_c is the fraction of those that establish interstellar communication, and L is the average length in years that civilizations continue to send communications.

The criticism is, of course, the high uncertainty of most of the variables. Over time, science can refine some of the variables. Others will remain speculative. The question was confined to the Milky Way because communication with remote galaxies is more difficult. Drake stated that the equation was written not to quantify the number of civilizations but to serve as talking points for the meeting.

The equation does define what scientists must learn to estimate the possibility of extraterrestrial life, and researchers have spent the last six decades assessing the variables. The first three variables, R_s, f_p, and N_e are amenable to scientific analysis, and considerable progress has been made in quantifying those variables. Drake and his colleagues initially estimated R_s as 1. The current NASA estimate is 1.5 to 3. Drake initially estimated f_p to be 0.2 to 0.5, or one-fifth to one-half of the stars have planets. Recent microlensing surveys suggest most stars have planets, and some more than one, so the current estimate is f_p is about 1. Drake estimated that there are 1 to 5 habitable planets per star with planets. That is now considered optimistic.

That life appeared reasonably quickly after Earth developed a favorable ecosystem is encouraging for f_l, which Drake estimated to be 1. The value for the remaining variables is a roll of the dice. Rational arguments result in just about any number you want. Drake felt the number of detectable civilizations between a thousand and one hundred million. Those who wish to believe we are unique can easily argue for a number less than 1.

SETI

The search for life in the universe, often using radio detection, is an old activity that proliferated beginning in the 1950s. SETI, an acronym for the Search for Extraterrestrial Intelligence, is used to describe such activities and as part of a name for numerous organizations and projects.

Both Nicola Tesla (1856 - 1943) and Guglielmo Marconi (1874 – 1937) attributed unexplained signals received by their equipment as possibly from a Martian civilization during a period of public fascination with life on the Red planet. Percival Lowell was publishing books with his sketches of canals on Mars. During August 21-23, 1924, during a close opposition of Mars, a National Radio Silence Day was promoted with 5 minutes of silence every hour on the hour for 36 hours to avoid interference with radio transmissions from Mars.

PROJECT	SPECTRUM	DATES
Radio Silence Day	N/A	Aug 21 - 23, 1924
Project Ozma	1.42 GHz	1960
Ohio State Big Ear	1.42 GHz	1973 - 1995
META, META II, BETA	1.4 – 1.7 GHz	1985 - 1999
MOP, Project Phoenix	1.2 – 3.0 GHz	1992 - 2004
Allen Telescope Array	1 – 15 GHz	2007 - present
SERENDIP	1.42 GHz, 0.4 – 5 GHz	1979 - present
Breakthrough Listen	Microwave, optical	2015 - present
Project Argus	1.4 to 1.7 GHz, other	1994 - present
Harvard Targeted Optical	Visible light	1998 - 2003
Harvard All-Sky Optical	Visible light	2006 - ????
Boquete Optical SETI	Visible Light	2010 - present
Automated Planet Finder	Visible light	2013 - present
Near-Infrared Optical SETI	Infrared	2015 -

The first attempt at SETI was Project Ozma conducted by Frank Drake at the NRAO for about 150 hours in April 1960. Ozma II was a second search with a large radio telescope that searched intermittently from 1972-1976. Professor John Kraus (1910-2004) at the University of Ohio constructed a large radio telescope called the Big Ear, which operated from 1973 – 1995. In August of 1977, astronomer Jerry Ehman was reviewing printout data from the Big Ear. A strong signal had been automatically recorded earlier, on August 15, 1977. Ehman circled the data and wrote *Wow!* in the margin because of the signal's strength. This became known as the *Wow!* Signal. It lasted for the entire 72 seconds that a fixed point in space would travel through one of the antenna feed horns. The antenna had two feed horns, but the signal was present in only one time slot. At that moment, the antenna was pointed toward Sagittarius in the general direction of the center of the Milky Way at the celestial declination -26°57'+-20' and

right ascension
19ʰ25ᵐ31ˢ+-10ˢ or
19ʰ28ᵐ22ˢ+-10ˢ (J2000)
depending on which horn
intercepted the signal.
This location is near the
5ᵗʰ magnitude star Tau
Sagittarii. Careful studies
eliminated the possibility
of known celestial

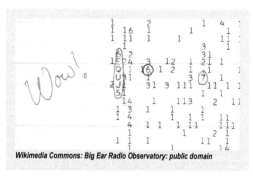

Wikimedia Commons: Big Ear Radio Observatory: public domain

sources. However, many follow-up searches in that area of the sky have revealed no new signals. One unverified incident leaves doubts, but the *Wow!* Signal remains a wow, and even to this day, an intriguing possibility.

Harvard University conducted the SETI projects META, META II, and BETA. In 1999, high winds destroyed the antenna supporting META. BETA and META II remain in operation with equipment upgraded in 1996.

One of the largest SETI organizations is the SETI Institute, formed in 1984 by Frank Drake and three other trustees. One of its early searches was Project Phoenix which organized time on the large radio telescopes Parks in Australia, Green Bank in West Virginia, and Arecibo in Puerto Rico. Today, the SETI Institute operates the Allan Telescope Array located in California. Initial donations by Paul Allen, Microsoft's co-founder, and Nathan Myhrvold, former Chief Technical Officer for Microsoft, helped launch this modern, high technology search. A later donation by Franklin Antonio, co-founder of Qualcomm, has helped upgrade the equipment. The Allan Array uses 42 antennas of 20-foot diameter and receivers covering 1 to 15 GHz, a broader range of frequencies than most searches.

Another well-funded and organized search is Breakthrough Listen, based at the Berkeley SETI Research Center at the University of California. Julia and Yuri Milner, Israeli-Russian entrepreneurs, funded this search. This program uses piggyback time on existing radio telescope infrastructure. This technique diverts signals from the host antenna used for other astronomical research and processes those diverted signals using SETI equipment.

For a while, Berkeley SETI Research Center sent chunks of data to individuals who had signed up to process data on their home computers in a program called SETI@home. The program ended in March 2020 due to several factors, including participants using their employer's computer assets and difficulty maintaining data quality control with so many participants.

Advanced civilizations could also use pulsed lasers to send light flashes toward us intentionally. Searching for light pulses is referred to as optical SETI. The laser transmitters' beamwidth and the field of view of optical telescopes that receive the signal are both narrow. The sender would need to direct the laser signal directly at us, and we would need to be looking in the correct direction to receive it. Optical SETI is also more susceptible to false detections as cosmic rays cause sporadic light flashes in the atmosphere, and radioactivity in glass can causes minute flashes. Nevertheless, communication at interstellar distances is possible, and numerous optical SETI projects exist.

To date, no extraterrestrial signal has been confirmed. Perhaps we are alone. Or maybe Calvin, in the 1989 Calvin and Hobbes cartoon, hit the nail on the head when he remarked, *"Sometimes I think the surest sign that intelligent life exists elsewhere in the universe is that none of it has tried to contact us."*

Active SETI

These searches bring up another 64-thousand-dollar question. The intentional act of transmitting signals toward an extraterrestrial target is referred to as active SETI or Messaging to Extraterrestrial Intelligence (METI). Listening for extraterrestrial signals seems safe enough, although detection could cause significant social upheaval. But should we transmit and give ourselves and our location away?

The question is moot. We have been transmitting radio signals for a century. Television, radio, radar, and other systems leak signals into space. Generally, these signals spread over space and would be very weak at interstellar distances. On the other hand, some transmissions are directed, such as spacecraft communications, and both the US and USSR have directed high-power radar signals at the planets, comets, and asteroids. A portion, indeed most, of this signal energy passes the target and continues deep into space. Notwithstanding Star Trek, interstellar travel is extremely difficult. Any civilization adequately advanced for interstellar travel could possibly detect even Earth's leaked signals.

A group of scientists met at a 2015 meeting of the American Association for the Advancement of Science to discuss if active SETI was wise. They released a statement that *"worldwide scientific, political, and humanitarian discussion must occur before any message is sent."*

It's too late. From 1974 to date, various organizations directed dozens of messages at multiple targets with no oversight. To read about an example first message from Earth that results from a haphazard approach to active SETI, Google "A Simple Response to an Elemental Message."

Search for Exoplanets

Planets around stars are referred to as exoplanets. Two Drake equation's unknowns are the fraction of stars with planets, f_p, and the average number of planets, N_e, of those stars with an ecosystem. The light from the host star completely swamps the tiny fraction of the light reflected from planets. Also, the angular separation of the planet and star is minute at interstellar distances. As a consequence of these factors, the direct detection of planets is challenging. By 2004, advancing telescope technology finally achieved the feat. The first direct observation of a planet was around the brown dwarf star, 2M1207, in the constellation Centaurus. The observation was in the infrared spectrum using the European Southern Observatory in Chile. That planet is giant with several Jupiter masses. As of 2020, multiple planets have been directly observed, but none smaller than Jupiter.

There are multiple indirect methods for observing exoplanets. The transit method detects a planet passing

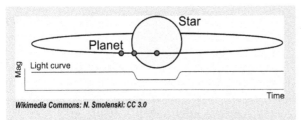

directly in front of a star's disk. The light curve parameters allow calculation of the semi-major axis, eccentricity and inclination of the orbit, the star's mass and radius, and the planet radius. The mass of the planet is also determined with the additional measurement of the star's radial velocity as it orbits the baryonic center of mass. The transit method requires precise alignment of the planet's orbital plane with our line of sight, and for an Earth-size planet orbiting at one au, the probability with random alignment is only 0.47%. In other words, most planets with parameters similar to Earth's would remain undetected.

The radial velocity method measures the star's velocity away and toward us as the star orbits around the center of mass of the star and planet. Doppler shift of the star's spectrum reveals the radial velocity of the star. Occasionally, the detection of the planet's spectrum provides a relatively complete set of parameters for both the star and planet.

Pulsars are small ultra-dense remnants of supernovas. These neutron stars emit extremely regular radio-signal pulses as they rotate rapidly. Like normal stars, when accompanied by a planet, they orbit about their common center of gravity. This changes the timing of the pulses. These first three methods favor the detection of larger, Jupiter-sized planets orbiting close to the parent star.

Another exoplanet discovery method involves detecting microlensing of a background star by a planet orbiting its parent star. The advantage of this technique is it works well for planets orbiting Sun-like stars at distances of one to ten au. The disadvantages are it requires very precise alignment. Because the Earth orbits the Sun, and stars are moving slightly with respect to each other, confirmation of the discovery with follow-up observations is impractical. The method works best in the direction of the Milky Way center, where background stars are numerous. The method provides an estimate of only the planet's mass and not orbital parameters.

Over sixty exoplanet search projects have been conducted. As of 2020, automated survey techniques using Earth-based telescopes have detected over 600 exoplanets, and space-based telescopes have detected over 2800 exoplanets. These numbers will grow with continued searches. Given that chance is required for favorable conditions for detection, the conclusion is obvious: many stars host planets.

Life on Mars

Despite the rapid waning of interest in space after Apollo, in the last 60 years, NASA has advanced technology and conducted critical science. NASA kept some interest afloat with the Space Shuttle. Then NASA began using two props; beautiful photoshopped celestial pictures and the search for life on Mars. We are absolute suckers for this alien thing, and due to some similarities to Earth, Mars is a great candidate for speculation. The Martian rovers Opportunity and Curiosity included multiple instruments to search for biological signatures and chemicals required by life forms. Even Mars orbiters have joined in the search. NASA frequently releases titillating news of a discovery of something necessary for life on Mars. But nothing has looked back into the cameras.

On the descent, the rover Opportunity released its heat shield, which then impacted the surface. Opportunity later visited the impact site and took this image. The heat shield

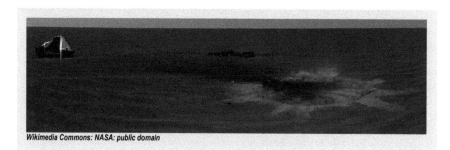

Wikimedia Commons: NASA: public domain

debris above and to the left of the impact crater is clearly visible.

With a lack of exciting news from Mars, NASA is researching and even planning to land missions to find life on Enceladus, the second moon of Saturn, Europa, the second moon of Jupiter, and Titan, the sixth moon of Saturn. The discovery of phosphine in the atmosphere of Venus in 2020 caused a stir. Phosphine, a compound of phosphorous and hydrogen, could be associated with life.

Panspermia

Panspermia from ancient Greek is derived from pan meaning "all" and sperma meaning "seed." Panspermia posits that life exists throughout the universe, spread by dust, meteorites, asteroids, and comets. Panspermia surfaced in Greek philosophy. The Swedish physicist and chemist Svante Arrhenius (1859 – 1927) formalized its study. Arrhenius won the 1903 Nobel Prize for Chemistry, and in 1908 wrote that human emission of CO_2 would prevent a new ice age and that a warmer Earth would be needed to feed a growing population. Fred Hoyle, whom I wrote about earlier, was a proponent of panspermia, as more recently was Stephen Hawking.

The idea of panspermia is reminiscent of the generally accepted theory that stars manufactured the heavier elements present in our bodies; those elements populated interstellar space and were constituents of our forming Solar system. Several scientists have suggested a real possibility of spores or bacteria hitchhiking on objects throughout the universe. NASA and the European Space Agency have conducted multiple experiments on the survivability of DNA, spores, bacteria, and microorganisms in space. Programs included the Long Duration Exposure Facility from 1984 to 1990, Exobiology Radiation Assembly from 1992 to 1993, BIOPAN from 1992 to 2007, and EXPOSE from 2008 to 2015. The conclusion is that radiation, UV light, and a vacuum rapidly destroy unprotected organisms. Still, organisms within even small bodies survive a long time, and some even survive the heat of atmospheric reentry.

Humans on Mars

Even unmanned space probes to Mars are risky business. The Soviet Union's first nine missions from 1960 to 1971 were either launch or spacecraft failures, and NASA's first attempt in 1964 was a launch failure. But NASA's Mariner 4 completed a successful flyby on July 15, 1965. Failures continue to this day, but 28 missions to Mars have been successful, and a few more were partially successful. The NASA lander Curiosity took this image from the surface of Mars in 2012. Today there are six members in the club of nations that sent spacecraft to Mars. Scientific exploration has included images, atmospheric analysis, finding mountains and past water-flow features, scooping up and sampling soil, examining the radiation environment, measuring magnetic fields, and detailed surveying. We've done about everything except returning a sample or setting foot on the planet.

So, will we step on Mars? To do so stretches the limits of technology, human endurance, and the national budget. The U.S. capability to launch astronauts languished for nearly a decade. With the loss of two Shuttles and their crew, the U.S. was caught flatfooted. The private company

Wikimedia Commons: NASA: public domain

SpaceX whose Crew Dragon spacecraft delivered astronauts to the ISS in May 2020, met this challenge. NASA is playing catch up with the Space Launch System. Even so, the most powerful planned rockets match, but do not exceed, the lift capability of the giant Saturn V rocket developed over 50 years ago. The following image is an artist's conception of an SLS rocket on the pad.

Wikimedia Commons: NASA: public domain

So back to the question, "Are we ready for Mars?" Werner Von Braun, the father of that giant Saturn 5 rocket, in 1952, first applied engineering principles to a planned mission to Mars. Since then, there have been over 60 serious plans by NASA, Russia, the European Union, and private enterprise for a manned mission to Mars. The basic technology is understood. The trick involves innovation to reduce the unimaginable scope of the undertaking. The distance to Mars exceeds that of the Moon by 500 times. Interestingly, for 70 years, every plan has predicted a crewed Mars mission in about 15 years. It's an ever-receding dream.

Travel time to the Moon by Apollo 11 was 62 hours, while a trip to Mars takes nine months. That's when Mars is closest to Earth, which happens every 26 months. What's worse, once there, the lowest energy approach requires waiting 26 months before heading back. The spacecraft must provide life support the whole time. With more powerful rockets, the total mission time could be as short as 400 days, but human endurance in space for that long is a challenge. The mind and body do not take kindly to zero gravity, stress, cramped space, and freeze-dried food for that long. Mars gravity is stronger than the Moon's, so more fuel is required to lift off Mars than the Moon.

The cost of the Apollo Moon program was just under 300 billion in today's dollars. Cost estimates for a crewed Mars mission range widely, but it's probably more than a trillion dollars. With the National debt at twenty-two trillion, increasing by a trillion a year, it's hard to imagine Congress appropriating sufficient funds soon for a Mars mission.

Direct launching of a manned spacecraft from Earth to Mars is beyond the capacity of any planned rocket. There are two possible approaches: one, assemble the equipment for the trip in Earth orbit, or two, assemble on the Moon. In 1989, NASA proposed to go back to the Moon, then onto Mars. NASA continues to kick the can down the road and suggests more modest missions. Recently, NASA again proposed we go back to the Moon to get to Mars. In 2019, at a White House celebration of Apollo 11, President Trump wisely asked a NASA official if going back to the Moon was necessary to get to Mars. As the official explained why it was required, standing in the background shaking his head, no, was Buzz Aldrin, the second man to walk on the Moon.

SpaceX corporation, founded by Elon Musk of Tesla fame, is planning Mars missions. Because of the trade imbalance, the U.S. is effectively transferring 400 billion dollars to China every year. If that problem isn't solved, the race to Mars could be between a private company and China.

Interstellar Travel

Oh, the dream: *"to go where no man has gone before."* Warp drive, light-speed, wormholes, and superluminal drives look pretty easy in science fiction. I remember when it wasn't so easy. Fifty years ago, I read Robert Heinlein's (1907 – 1988) book, *Starman Jones*. The jump to light speed wasn't so easy then. The jump involved heroic mathematical calculations, by a hero, of course, least you pop out in the middle of a planet.

Well, folks, the jump to light speed isn't going to happen, nor is interstellar travel in the lifetime of men or women. The trip may begin on an ark, but only their offspring would arrive. Let's work out a few painful details.

It's 4.2 light-years to even the closest star, Proxima Centauri. Traveling at the fastest speed man has ever traveled, Apollo 10 at 24,816 mph, it would take 115,000 years to reach Proxima Centauri. As you can see, the need is speed. Let's kick our spacecraft up to 90% of the speed of light. At that speed, a trip to Proxima Centauri would require just under 4.7 years. Einstein gives the crew a break. At that speed, it's only two years for them. With an identical return trip, everyone on Earth will have aged 9.4 years, while our travelers will have aged four years.

But let's consider a few more details. Do you remember those cramped Apollo spacecraft? Their mass was 50 tons when they left Earth orbit for the Moon. That 50 tons included enough life support for two weeks, not two years. It gets worse! Accelerating 50 tons to 90% the speed of light requires the expenditure of 4.6×10^{14} kilowatt-hours of energy. That is roughly three times the total energy generated worldwide in 2020. Furthermore, all those dams, fossil-fuel powerplants, nuclear plants, wind farms, and solar panels would need to be on board the spacecraft that weighs only 50 tons. The required energy assumes our explorers aren't coming back, and they won't be decelerating to stop. This energy estimate also ignores the drag of all the interstellar gas and the fact that it becomes radiation at those speeds. If they hit anything the size of a

grain of sand, the released energy is that of an atomic bomb. Near light-speed travel is no trip to the Moon.

In 1995, the Mexican theoretical physicist Miguel Alcubierre (1964 – present) came up with a nifty idea: don't move the spacecraft, instead move space. He manipulated the field equations of General Relativity to contract space in front of the spacecraft and expand space to the rear. The spacecraft remains in an unaccelerated flat spacetime, and the occupants don't feel a thing. Soon, you're over there. Well, mathematical gymnastics got a name for Alcubierre, but unfortunately, it requires non-existent exotic materials. Perhaps dilithium crystals would do the trick.

So, near-light speed is out. The remaining solution is the ark—thousands of years in space to a single destination. The destination had better be chosen wisely. Perhaps it would be best to wait for advancing technology to verify a green planet robotically. Perhaps it would be best to wait further so the technology can get humans there quicker. The timing game is tricky. By waiting still longer, a second more advanced ark could pass the first, the third could pass the second, and so on.

The hazards of long periods in space and the mass requirement for long-term life support make interstellar missions essentially impossible. This reduces the options to crewless probes. Project Daedalus, Project Icarus, and Project Longshot studied unmanned, heavy interstellar probes that used nuclear fusion propulsion to reach small fractions of the speed of light so that the mission completes within an earthbound human lifetime. Despite billions of dollars in research over seven decades, science is not close to practical fusion power on Earth, let alone onboard a spacecraft.

Project Dragonfly, Breakthrough Starshot, Starlight, and Starwisp studied sails to reflect light or microwave radiation from Earth or near-Earth based transmitter. This reflected energy propels the sail-driven probe toward its target. Because the delivered thrust is small, these approaches use miniature-sized probes. It seems mankind is not very patient. Both the nuclear-propelled massive probes and the miniature probes have one design feature in common: fast speeds to reduce travel time to less than a human lifespan, and typically to the nearest known planet, Proxima Centauri b.

Directed panspermia is the purposeful seeding of life, either directed to Earth or directed away from Earth. The idea of suspended animation and embryo transport as a solution to the mass and time of travel problems is a frequent topic of science fiction. The technology of recovering frozen embryos without a parent host is a potential way to colonize other worlds. However, the intentional seeding of other worlds with either basic or intelligent life forms raises serious ethical issues.

The alien question is two distinctly different questions, and the two answers have vastly different probabilities. Do aliens exist? My answer: probably so. If not, *"it's an awful waste of space."* Have they visited us? My answer: probably not. It's too far from any neighbor's back door.

That's all Folks

It's a pretty good bet we won't settle anywhere else. If the expanding and warming Sun doesn't get us in a billion years, some other existential threat, including ourselves, probably will. God gave us a nice place. Our story began here, and it will end here. And, so does my story.

Step outside and look up: Astronomy is Heavenly.

11 Resources

Would you like to explore the Heavens more deeply?
The chapter is a short list of some of my favorite resources
for the further enjoyment of the Heavens.

Books

There are hundreds of worthy books covering science, astronomy, and cosmology. Listed here are a few of my favorites and a brief description of each.

Coming of Age in the Milky Way by Timothy Ferris is a well-spun tale of Astronomy's history from ancient times to the turn of the 21st century. It's a fun read: a mixture of good literature and good science.

Cosmos by Carl Sagan is a book companion to the popular television series Cosmos. It's hard to believe these works are now forty years old. They are still relevant today. The book is an interesting mixture of Sagan speculation and science and Sagan's fascination with life and space.

Einstein: His Life and Universe by Walter Isaacson interweaves Einstein's biography with a readable and commendable description of his two theories of relativity, his battle against quantum weirdness, and his failed quest to unite the theories of gravity and electromagnetism.

While the previous three books cover astronomy's history and science from a spectator sport perspective, the following four are designed more for the active participant who steps outside after dark and uses optical aid to enjoy the Heavens.

Touring the Universe through Binoculars by Philip S. Harrington is also a great start if you wish to practice with a pair of binoculars before investing in a telescope. *NightWatch* by Terence Dickinson is a general guide as you progress in amateur astronomy. *The Messier Objects* by

Stephen J. O'Meara is a more in-depth look at the ever-popular Messier objects.

Burnham's Celestial Handbook by Robert Burnham, Jr., is a three-volume set published in 1977. Although dated, Burnham describes in detail every object you'll ever see in your new telescope. Burham's and O'Meara's books are must-have books once you purchase a telescope.

Magazines

Two leading astronomy magazines are *Sky & Telescope* and *Astronomy*. The byline of *Sky & Telescope* magazine is *"The essential guide to astronomy."* It's a fair claim, as both amateur and professional astronomers read it. It covers current research, events in the sky, and equipment. The byline of *Astronomy* magazine is *"The world's best-selling astronomy magazine."* It also includes reporting on current science, celestial events, and observing tips and guides. These magazines are a great way to stay updated on recent research, events, and equipment.

Clubs

Astronomy clubs are a great way to begin an adventure in astronomy. They often have public viewings through telescopes belonging to the members. These events are usually open to the public. Even if the club is not holding an "officially public" star party, if you show up and say you are interested in astronomy, they'll welcome you with open arms. The NASA Jet Propulsion Lab at the California Institute of Technology maintains a website with a locator for the nearest club to you. The website also has a calendar of additional live and online events. The website is *nightsky.jpl.nasa.gov/index.cfm*

Public Planetariums

Planetariums are theatres with a dome ceiling and projector that simulate the night sky. Although they are not the real thing, planetariums can be very realistic. Furthermore, they have the advantage of not being restricted to "now." Not only can they demonstrate the sky of the past and future, but they can also illustrate motion in the sky by running time forward or backward at any speed. They are comfortable, and you have a guide for the program. Pictured here is the

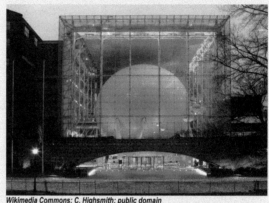
Wikimedia Commons: C. Highsmith: public domain

Hayden Sphere at the Rose Center in New York City. The top half of the sphere is the dome for a planetarium theatre, and the bottom half is a second theatre with a screen measuring 36-feet in diameter.

Attending a planetarium program is a great family outing. Programs may include what's in the sky tonight, making a great introduction before taking your new telescope outside. Some planetarium programs are free, while some have a modest fee. Planetariums are common, with too many to list here. To find a planetarium near you, go to *en.wikipedia.org/wiki/List_of_planetariums*.

Planisphere

The Earth's daily rotation on its axis and its orbit around the Sun causes the celestial sphere to change constantly. To be valid, star maps must be printed for a specific latitude, date, and time. A clever solution to this problem that I used as a boy is called a planisphere. You

Wikimedia Commons: H. Raab: CC 3.0

turn an inner ring to place the current time adjacent to the printed date on an outer ring. The window then has a map of the Heavens. A flat map of objects that are actually on the celestial hemisphere introduces distortion. Also, the star map changes with the observer's latitude, so planispheres are available for a range of latitudes, such as 30° to 40°N. But they work well enough to do the job. Planispheres are still available, but smartphone apps are rapidly replacing them.

Desktop Planetariums

Another definition for planetarium is an app, software program, or website that simulates the night sky. When planning your night's session, the large screen, keyboard, and mouse of laptops or desktop computers are hard to beat. You can easily change the date, hour of the night, viewing direction, and search for objects of interest.

The SkyX is a commercial Windows or macOS subscription-based software planetarium program offered in three levels: Student, Serious Astronomer, and Professional. Advanced tools for telescope control and imaging are also available.

Starry Night is a commercial Windows or macOS software planetarium program offered in four levels: CSAP, Enthusiast, Pro, and Pro Plus. Educational products for elementary through high-school grades are also available.

Stellarium is a free, open-source, advanced planetarium project for Windows, macOS, and Linux. I recommend some computer experience for installing Stellarium.

App Planetariums

Smartphone planetariums are handy under the Heavens at night. Smart-phone planetariums are often available in free, ad-supported forms and commercial versions with more features. Simply pointing the phone at an object in the Heavens displays a celestial map and labels the desired and nearby objects. There could hardly be an easier way to learn to identify the planets, stars, and constellations.

Author

The app *Star Tracker* by PYOPYO Studio is concise at 64 MB on my Android, fast opening and running, and visually stunning. With default settings, this app flashes many meteors across the screen, which are only for effect and not real. For me, this is rather annoying, but fortunately, you can turn this off in the settings. *Star Tracker* does not have time and date control in the free version.

Another popular app is *Star Walk 2* by Vito Technology. It requires more memory and loads and runs slower on my older Android smartphone. You can set the date and time in the free version, and you may purchase additional databases such as comets and artificial satellites.

SkySafari by Simulation Curriculum is a commercial planetarium app for mobile devices and desktops. It's rather large at 312 MB on my Android, but it runs fast. Shown here is a screen of *SkySafari* with the date and time editor open. Simulation Curriculum also publishes a version for laptops and desktops running Windows and macOS.

Web-based Planetariums

Web-based planetariums are websites that simulate the view of the Heavens at any place or time. There's no need to install software on your device.

One such website is *TheSkyLive.com*. This site not only includes a planetarium, but it also has helpful observing guides and information on a variety of objects and events, including the constellations, the planets, comets, and near-Earth object (NEO) passes.

Google Sky is a form of an online planetarium for displaying images of celestial objects. It's not a planetarium program in the sense that it lacks features such as viewing controls, time and date settings, or position display of solar systems objects. It's not intended to help you find objects in the night sky.

Another online planetarium is *In-the-Sky.org*. It has convenient viewing controls and is very easy to use. The aesthetics of the screen are not as pleasing as other planetarium programs.

General Websites

For information about a particular subject, my go-to source is *Wikipedia*. It contains over 30,000 articles covering astronomy. *Category: Astronomy* is a Wikipedia page with a list of subject subcategories in astronomy. Each subcategory includes links to specific pages.

Heavens-Above is my choice for forecasting artificial satellite passes, including the International Space Station. This site also includes many other helpful pages, including a planisphere-style planetarium.

Space.com is all things space and astronomy. Think of it as an online magazine organized by topic. The home page is news and links to other resources at the site.

Resellers

Buying a long-tube, small-aperture telescope on a rickety mount from a department store is a sure way to kill a child's or your interest in astronomy. Your first telescope doesn't need to be, nor should it be, expensive. However, I recommend buying it from a telescope dealer who can give you good advice, regardless of your budget. The following list is not an endorsement of any dealer, but these resellers specialize in optics.

Adorama, New York, NY, (800)223-2500, *adorama.com*

Agena Astroproducts, Cerritos, CA, (562)215-4473, *agendaastro.com*

Astronomics, Norman, OK (800)422-7876, *astronomics.com*

B&H, New York, NY, (800)221-5743, *bhphotovideo.com*

Focus, Brooklyn, NY, (800)221-0828, *focuscamera.com*

High Point Scientific, Montague, NJ, (800)266-9590, *highpointscientific.com*

Khan Scope, Toronto, ON, (800)580-7160, *khanscope.com*

Mile High Astronomy, Denver, CO, (877)279-5280, *milehighastro.com*

OPT, Carlsbad, CA, (800)483-6287, *optcorp.com*

Optics Planet, Northbrook, IL (800)504-5897, *opticsplanet.com*

Woodland Hills, Woodland Hills, CA, (818)347-2270, *whcamera.com*

12 Appendix

Greek Alphabet

LOWER	LETTER	UPPER
α	alpha	A
β	beta	B
γ	gamma	Γ
δ	delta	Δ
ε	epsilon	E
ζ	zeta	Z
η	eta	H
θ	theta	Θ
ι	iota	I
κ	kappa	K
λ	lambda	Λ
μ	mu	M
ν	nu	N
ξ	xi	Ξ
o	omicron	O
π	pi	Π
ρ	rho	P
σ	sigma	Σ
τ	tau	T
υ	upsilon	Y
φ	phi	Φ
χ	chi	X
ψ	psi	Ψ
ω	omega	Ω

Glossary

absolute magnitude An object's apparent magnitude viewed from a distance of 10 parsecs, or 32.6 ly.

accretion disk A disk-shaped collection of material orbiting around a massive body.

aphelion The point of farthest distance in the orbit of an object around the Sun.

apogee The point of furthest distance in the orbit of an object around the Earth.

apparent magnitude The brightness of an object when viewed from Earth. Each 2.5X reduction in brightness reduces the scale by 1. The dimmest visible star in dark skies is about 6. Often shortened to magnitude.

asterism A pattern formed by multiple stars.

astronomical unit (au) A unit of distance equal to the average Sun-Earth distance. The standard is 92,956,000 miles, 4.8481×10^{-6} parsecs, and 1.5813×10^{-5} ly.

azimuth Angular measure eastward from the north around the horizon.

barycenter The center of mass about which two objects orbit.

baryonic matter Familiar baryon particles are protons and neutrons which make up the nucleus of an atom. Matter in the universe that has been directly detected is baryonic. The proposed dark matter is perhaps non-baryonic.

celestial equator An extension of the Earth's equator onto the celestial sphere.

celestial pole An extension of the rotational axis of the Earth onto the celestial sphere.

circumpolar A region near the north or south celestial pole in which celestial objects never set. The extent of the region depends on the observer's latitude.

conjunction Two or more celestial objects in visual proximity.

culmination The moment a celestial object crosses the observer's meridian.

declination The angular coordinates north or south of the celestial equator, from +90° (north) to -90° (south).

Doppler shift A frequency shift of an electromagnetic wave due to the emitting object's radial velocity. For light, it's measured by spectral analysis.

eccentricity A measure of orbital deviation from a true circle. 0 is circular, 0 to 1 are elliptical, 1 is parabolic, and greater than 1 is hyperbolic.

ecliptic The path of the Sun on the celestial sphere.

elongation The angular separation of an object from the Sun as viewed from Earth.

equinox The biannual moment when the Sun crosses the celestial equator. Day and night are the same lengths everywhere on Earth.

gas giant A large planet composed primarily of hydrogen and helium. Jupiter and Saturn are solar system examples.

geocentric Centered on the Earth.

geostationary orbit An orbit directly above the Earth's equator with a period equal to the Earth's rotation period. An object in a geostationary orbit appears motionless from the Earth.

H II region A region with a concentration of partially ionized hydrogen where stars commonly form.

heliocentric Centered on the Sun.

ice giant A large planet composed of ices of elements heavier than hydrogen and helium. Uranus and Neptune are solar system examples.

inclination The angular tilt of an orbit to a reference plane. One reference plane is the invariable plane which is the "average" plane of all the planets.

Julian year Exactly 365.25 days of 24 hours.

light-year The distance light travels in a Julian year, approximately 5,879,000,000,000 miles, 5.879×10^{12} miles.

magnitude See apparent magnitude.

main sequence A band on the Hertzsprung-Russell diagram where stars spend the majority of their life.

meridian An imaginary line running north-south across the sky and passing through the zenith directly overhead.

metallicity The abundance of elements heavier than hydrogen and helium present in an object.

molecular cloud An interstellar cloud of primarily non-ionized molecular gas such as hydrogen. Once stars form, they partially ionize the cloud into visible H II regions.

occultation An event where a foreground object blocks the view of a more distant object. The Moon blocking a planet is an example.

opposition The time when two celestial objects are on opposite sides of the sky. When a planet and the Sun are in opposition, the planet is at its closest to Earth.

parallax The shift in the apparent position of a nearer object with respect to a further object when the viewpoint is shifted.

parsec The distance of an object when its angular parallax is one arcsecond from two extremes of the Earth's orbit.

penumbra The partial shadow by the Earth during a lunar eclipse.

perigee The closest approach of an object in Earth orbit.

precession A periodic shift in the orientation of a rotational axis.

proper motion The rate of angular motion over time. The stars are slowly and randomly changing their position on the celestial sphere.

radial velocity The velocity of an object along the line of sight, usually determined by the Doppler shift.

redshift Spectral shift of color toward the red caused by objects receding from the measurer.

retrograde motion The motion of an object in an unexpected direction. Most solar system bodies orbit in the same direction because of the system's initial angular momentum. Some orbit in retrograde. Near opposition, the outer planets appear to move in retrograde because the Earth's orbit overtakes the outer planet.

semi-major axis One-half of the diameter of an elliptical orbit's long axis.

sidereal year The time it takes the Earth to complete one orbit with respect to the stars, currently 365.256363 days of 24 hours. A sidereal day is 23 hours, 56 minutes, 4.0905 seconds.

solar mass A unit of mass equal to the Sun's mass, 1.98847×10^{30} kg, or 4.3838×10^{30} pound-mass.

spectrograph An instrument that spreads an electromagnetic wave into a spectrum for detailed analysis.

synodic day The time it takes the Earth to rotate once on its axis as viewed from the Sun. Also called a solar day. Its mean value is 24 hours.

umbra The full shadow by the Earth during a lunar eclipse.

zenith The point directly overhead on the north-south meridian line.

zodiac A band approximately 8° north and south of the ecliptic that contains the constellations where the Sun and planets wander.

Units, Acronyms, and Abbreviations

AD is an acronym of anno Domini, Medieval Latin for in the year of the Lord. Devised in 525 AD. Dates in this book are assumed to be AD unless followed by BC.

au is an acronym for Astronomical Unit, a unit of distance equal to the average Earth-Sun distance, roughly 93 million miles.

Az is an abbreviation for azimuth, an angular measurement in the horizontal plane, clockwise from north. East is 90°, south 180°, etc.

BC is an acronym of Before Christ. Popularized first in 1627 in French as ante Christum.

CMB is an acronym of the Cosmic Microwave Background radiation, a remnant of the Big Bang.

CSM is an acronym of the Command Service Module, a component of the Apollo spacecraft.

DEC is an abbreviation of declination. Declination is an angular measurement north or south of the celestial equator.

DNA is an acronym of Deoxyribonucleic Acid, the genetic building code of living organisms.

EDT is an acronym of Eastern Daylight Times. Forms exist for other daylight and standard time zones.

El is an abbreviation for elevation. The elevation is an angular measurement in a vertical plane from zero at the horizon to 90° at the zenith.

ESA is an acronym of the European Space Agency, an intergovernmental organization of 22 member states and associates.

EVA is an acronym for Extra-Vehicular Activity or spacewalks.

f(number) is an optical term signifying the "speed" of a system, equal to the focal length of a lens divided by the effective aperture.

FOV is an acronym for Field Of View.

GMT is an acronym of Greenwich Mean Time, the mean solar time at the Royal Observatory in Greenwich, London, the Prime meridian. GMT is a synonym for UTC, Universal Coordinated Time.

H II is a symbol for ionized (stripped of an electron) atomic hydrogen.

HST is an acronym for the Hubble Space Telescope.

H-R is an acronym of the Hertzsprung-Russell diagram, a plot of absolute magnitude versus color and temperature.

IAU is an acronym of the International Astronomical Union.

IC(number) is the Index Catalogue of Nebulae and Clusters of Stars. Published in 1895 and 1908, it's an update to the NGC catalog.

IR is an acronym of Infra-Red.

ISS is an acronym for the International Space Station.

JPL is an acronym of the Jet Propulsion Lab, a federally funded research lab and NASA field center in California.

JWST is an acronym of the James Webb Space Telescope.

LEM is an acronym of the Lunar Excursion Module, the Apollo spacecraft section that landed on the lunar surface.

LIGO is an acronym for Laser Interferometer Gravitational-wave Observatory. Interferometry is the combination of two or more separated instruments into one effectively larger instrument.

LMC is an acronym of Large Magellanic Cloud, a local dwarf galaxy.

ly is an abbreviation for light-year, a unit of distance equal to 5.879×10^{12} miles.

METI is an acronym for Messaging Extraterrestrial Intelligence, the active form of SETI.

mm is an abbreviation for millimeter, the unit of length equal to 1/1000 of a meter. There are 25.4 mm in an inch.

M(number) is the Messier catalog of non-stellar celestial objects.

MOND is an acronym of Modified Newtonian Dynamics, an unverified alternative theory to dark matter.

mph is an abbreviation for miles per hour, a unit of speed.

NASA is an acronym of the National Aeronautics and Space Administration.

NEO is an acronym of Near-Earth Object, any solar system body that has or could pass within 1.3 au of Earth.

NGC(number) is an entry in the New General Catalogue of Nebulae and Clusters of Stars, first published in 1888.

NRAO is an acronym of the National Radio Astronomy Observatory, which operates numerous radio telescopes.

PA is an acronym of Position Angle, an angular measurement clockwise from north of one object from another in the FOV of a telescope.

pc is an abbreviation for parsec, a unit of distance that results in 1 arcsecond of parallax for a baseline of 1 au. One parsec is roughly 3.26 ly.

RCT is an acronym for the Ritchey-Chrétien Telescope.

RTG is an acronym of Radioisotope Thermoelectric Generator, a power source with no moving parts that uses the heat of radioactive decay to generate electricity.

SETI is an acronym for the Search for Extraterrestrial Intelligence.

SLS is an acronym for NASA's Space Launch System.

SMC is an acronym of the Small Magellanic Cloud, a local dwarf galaxy.

UGC(number) is an acronym for the Uppsala General Catalogue of Galaxies visible from the Northern Hemisphere, first published in 1973.

UFO is an acronym for Unidentified Flying Object.

USAF is an acronym for the United States Air Force.

UTC is an acronym of Coordinated Universal Time, a successor to and synonym of GMT. It's approximately the local mean time at the Prime meridian.

UV is an acronym for Ultraviolet light.

ZHR is an acronym for Zenith Hourly Rates, the number of visible meteors per hour looking straight up in dark skies.

13 The Images

The Great Library of Alexandria, Egypt, was the most extensive library of the ancient world. It became a great center for knowledge and learning. It held perhaps as many as 400,000 scrolls. A decline began a century before Christ and continued during the Roman period. Little was left by 260 AD.

Wikipedia

Two millennia later, the Internet was born, and in 2001, Wikipedia launched. By 2020, Wikipedia contained 6 million articles in English and 50 million articles in 309 languages. Wikipedia writers and editors, including your author, are an open community. Anyone can register, and after a brief apprenticeship, begin to publish and edit articles on Wikipedia. This invites criticism concerning the accuracy and bias of articles. But articles are openly reviewed and edited by the community. A study by the science journal *Nature* determined that the accuracy of Wikipedia and *Encyclopedia Britannica* are similar.

My copies of *Sky & Telescope* magazine, my old college textbook *Principles of Astronomy* by Stanley Wyatt, the three volumes of *Burnham's Celestial Handbook*, and Wikipedia were my primary sources for this book. Most of the graphics in this book are from Wikimedia Commons, a repository of images. *"A picture is worth a thousand words"* is paraphrased from an initial remark by Henrik Ibsen, a Norwegian playwright (thank you Wiki for that knowledge). Wikimedia Commons images greatly enhanced this book.

The images are identified by copyright use. Some of the images are in the public domain. Others are used under

Creative Common (CC) by attribution (BY) pursuant to
ShareAlike (SA) processes, versions 2.0, 2.5, 3.0, and 4.0.
For example, an image marked CC 2.0 is used under the CC
BY-SA 2.0 license.

Index

Aurora, **42**

A

accretion, 92
Active SETI, **226**
Age of Enlightenment, 9
Al Sufi, 188
Albategnius, 77
Al-Battani, 77
Alcubierre, 234
Aldrin, 233
Aliens, **219**
Allen, 225
Almagest, 2
al-Sufi, 2
Anders, 70, 85
Andromeda, **176**
    galaxy, 176
annular eclipse, 81
Apollo
    mission, **84**, 232
    spacecraft, **86**
apple, 22
Aristarchus, 4, 15
Aristotle, 3, 4
Arnold, 220
Arp, 198
Arrhenius, 230
Artificial Satellites, **35**
    Observing, **38**
As the World Turns, **28**
Asteroids, **107**
Atiacensis, 77
Atom, **12**
au, 14
Auriga, **185**

B

Baade, 130, 210
Baily, 81
Barnard, 127
baryonic matter, 217
Bayer, 131, 135
Belanger, 15
Big Bang, **211**
    chronology, **213**
    resistance, **215**
Big Numbers, **11**
Binoculars, **48**
Biot, 151
Black Holes, **140**
Bohr, 25
Bok, 153
Bonnet, 107
Book of Fixed Stars, 2, 188
Books, Recommended, **237**
Borman, 70, 85
Brahe, 4, 139
Bright Stars, **136**
Burney, 117

C

Calandrelli, 15
Calvin and Hobbes, 226
Cassegrain, 53
Cassini, 113
Cassiopeia, **178**
Catalogues
    Messier, 145

Other, **153**
Cavendish, 20
Celestial Coordinates, **56**
Cepheids, **207**
Ceres, 107
Cernan, 88
Chaffee, 85, 131
chaos, 21
Chrétien, 53
chromatic distortion, 51
circumpolar, 33
Clark, 37
Clark Belt, **37**
Clavius, 77
Clubs, Astronomy, **238**
Clusters
    Globular, **146**
    Open, **145**
Collide, 206
Collinder, 184
Columbus, 78
Comets, **120**
Conjunctions, **113**
Constellation
    88, The, **156**
    Andromeda, **176**
    Auriga, **185**
    Cassiopeia, **178**
    Cygnus, **173**
    Gemini, **159**
    Hercules, **168**
    History, **155**
    Leo, **163**
    list, 156
    Lyra, **169**
    Orion, **183**
    Pegasus, **175**
    Perseus, **180**
    Sagittarius, **171**
    Scorpius, **166**
    Southern, **187**
    Taurus, **181**
    Ursa Major, **161**
    Ursa Minor, **165**
Coordinated Universal Time, **29**
Copernican Revolution, **3**
Copernicus, 3, 74

cosmic microwave background,
    214
cosmological constant, 209
Crossen, 50
Curtis, 195
Cygnus, **173**

D

d'Ailly, 78
da Vinci, 75
Dalton, 13
dark matter, 3
Dark Matter, **216**
Dark Nebula, **152**
Darwin, 123
de Lacaille, 156, 187
De Revoltionibus Orbium
    Coelestium, 3
de Vaucouleurs, 197
Deep Field, **204**
Democritus, 12
Determinism, **21**
Dicke, 213
Diderot, 9
Dirac, 10, 210
Distance Units, **14**
Doppler shift, 17, 127
Drake, 222, 225
Drake Equation, **222**
Draper, 131
Dreyer, 153, 187

E

Early Astronomy, **1**
Earth
    density, 27
    magnetic field, 42
    rotation, 28
    seasons, 31
Eclipse
    Binary Stars, **133**
Eclipses
    Lunar, **78**
    Solar, **80**
Eclipsing Binaries, **133**

Ecliptic, **34**, **97**
Eddington, 82, 94, 124, 215
Ehman, 224
Einstein, 25
  biggest blunder, 210
  disliked expansion theory, 209
  E=mc², 124
  General Relativity, 23
  induction vs deduction, 67
  matter energy relation, 11
  modified Newton's laws, 216
  motion, 4
  Nobel Prize, **24**
  quantum, 25
  quotes, 19, 25, 26, 68, 215
  relativity, 6, 22
  Rings, **205**
  Special Relativity, 22
  theory confirmation, 82, 102
Electromagnetic Waves, **19**
Emission Nebula, **148**
Epicycles, **2**
  Death of, **5**
Equinox, **32**
Eratosthenes, 27
ether, 19
evening star, 101
exit pupil, 49
Exoplanets
  Search for, **227**
Expanding Universe, **209**
eye relief, 49

F

false color, 51
Fata Morgana mirage, 221
Fermi, 219
Feynman, 25
field of view, 49
fission, 94
Flamsteed, 131
Fraunhofer, 16, 194
Friedman, 209
fusion, 94

G

Gaia, 16
Galaxy
  Local Group, **199**
  Observing, **200**
  Types, **196**
Galilean moons, 109
Galileo
  Milky Way is stars, 193
  Moon's beauty, 72
  observation of Neptune, 117
Galileo Galilei, **6**
Galle, 116
gedankenexperiment, 22
Gemini, **159**
General Theory of Relativity, 23
geostationary, 37
Globular Clusters, **146**
Gravity, **21**
Gravity and Inertia, **23**
Gravity Waves, **66**
Great Telescopes, **58**
Gregory XIII, 77
Grissom, 85
Guiducci, 7

H

H II regions, 125
Hale, 58, 195
Hall, 105
Halley, 120, 127
Harrington, 50
Hawking, 230
Heinlein, 233
heliocentric, 4
helium, 17
Hercules, **168**
Herschel, John
  travel to South Africa, 187
Herschel, William
  catalogue of Nebulae, 153
  discovery of Uranus, 107, 115
Hertz, 67, 218
Hertzsprung, 128
Hevelius, 156

Heywood, 144
Higgs boson, 14
Hipparchus, 15
Hodges, 42
How Big is the Heavens, **15**
How to Buy a Telescope, **54**
How to Use a Telescope, **57**
Hoyle, 211, 230
H-R diagram, 129, 137
Hubble Deep Field, **204**
Hubble Space Telescope, 62
Hubble, Edwin, 201, 209
    coined Local Group term, 199
    discovery of expansion, 59
    galaxy classification, 196
    namesake of HST, 62
Huggins, 194
Humans on Mars, **231**
Humason, 209
Huygens, 58

I

ice age, 96
inertia, 20
inflationary period, **213**
Inquisition, 7
International Dark-Sky
    Association, 45
Interstellar Travel, **233**
irradiance, 134
Isaac Newton. *See* Newton
ISS, 39

J

Jansky, 60
Janssen, 17
Jastrow, 216
Juno, 107
Jupiter, **109**

K

Kant, 194
Kelvin, 123

Kennedy, 84, 88
Kepler, 5, 30, 102
Kneller, 9
Kraus, 224
Kuiper Belt, **119**

L

Laplace
    determinism, 21
    nebula theory, 193
    solar system formation, 92
laws of planetary motion, 6
Le Verrier, 116
Leavitt, 207
Lemaitre, 209
Leo, **163**
Let There Be Light, **213**
Life on Mars, **229**
Light, **16**
Light Pollution, **44**
    absent in antiquity, 1
    doesn't diminish Moon, 75
light-year, 15
Local Group, **199**
Lockyer, 17
Lovell, 70, 85
Lowell, 105, 118
Low-Hanging Fruit, **66**
Lunar Eclipses, **78**
ly, 15
Lyra, **169**

M

Magazines, **238**
Magellan, 187
Magnitude, **18**
    absolute, 18
    apparent, 18
Marconi, 223
Marius, 110
Mars, **104**
    Humans on, **231**
    Life on, **229**
Mass, **19**
Maunder minimum, 96

Maxwell, 19
Mechain, 145
Mercury, **100**
Messier, Charles, **144**
Meteors, **40**
Milky Way, **143**
MOND, 217
Moon, **69**
  Formation, **71**
  Observing, **72**
  Through a Telescope, **75**
morning star, 101
Morrison, 215
Musk, 233
Myhrvold, 225

N

NASA, 84
Nebula
  Dark, **152**
  Emission, **148**
  Mystery, **193**
  Planetary, **149**
Neptune, **116**
Newton, **8**
  color in telescopes, 51
  fails relativity laws, 216
  formula for gravity, 22
  laws of motion, 36
  Newton's cannon, 35
  planetary motion error, 102
  reflecting telescope, 53
North Star, 2
Nova, 4, **138**

O

Observing
  Galaxy, **200**
  ISS, 39
  Jupiter, **110**
  lunar eclipses, 78
  Mars, **105**
  Moon, **72**
  Multiple Stars, **132**
  satellites, 38

Saturn, **112**
Solar Eclipses, **82**
Uranus, 116
Venus, 103
Oort Cloud, **119**
Open Clusters, **145**
opposition, 105
Optics, **47**
Orion, **183**
Orion Nebula, **124**, **125**

P

Pallas, 107
Panspermia, **230**
parallax, 14
parsec, 14
Parsons, 203
Pegasus, **175**
penumbra, 79
Penzias, 214
Perseus, **180**
Piazzi, 107
Pigafetta, 187
Plancius, 156
Planck, 25
Planet, **99**
  inferior, 100
  Jupiter, **109**
  Mars, **104**
  Mercury, **100**
  Neptune, **116**
  Pluto, **117**
  Saturn, **111**
  Uranus, **115**
  Venus, **102**
Planetariums
  Laptop and Desktop, **240**
  Public, **239**
  Smartphone Apps, **241**
  Web-Based, **242**
Planetary Nebula, **149**
Planisphere, **239**
Plato, 73
Pluto, **117**
  reduction in rank, 91, 119
Polaris, 2, **32**

Pope, 60
Precession, **34**
Principia, 9
Proper Motion, **126**
Ptolemy
    Almagest, 2, 130
    constellation names, 156
    distance to Moon, 69
Pulsars, **139**, 228
pyramids, 2

Q

quantum mechanics, 25
quark, 13

R

radiant, 41
Radio Telescopes, **60**
Reber, 60
Relativity, **22**
Resellers, **243**
Ritchey, 195
RTG, 122
Rubin, 217
Ruppelt, 220
Russel, 128
Rutherford, 13, 67, 124

S

Sagan, 142, 222
Sagittarius, **171**
Saturn, **111**
Saturn V, **88**
Schmitt, 88
Schwartzchild, 141
Science, **9**
    beauty, 11
    definition, 10
    Low-Hanging Fruit, **66**
scientific notation, 12
Scientific Revolution, 7, 9
Scorpius, **166**
Seasons, **31**

SETI, **223**
    Active, **226**
Shapley, 195
Shepard, 84
shower, meteor, 41
sidereal
    day, 29
    year, 30
simultaneous, 23
Skywalker, 131
Slipher, 209
Solar Dynamics Obs., 95
Solar Eclipses, **80**
    Observing, **82**
Solar System, **91**
    Formation, **92**
Solstice, **32**
Southern Sky, **187**
Space Telescopes, **62**
SpaceX, 233
Special Theory of Relativity, 22
spectrograph, 16
standard model, 13
Star of the East, 114
Star Stuff, **141**
Star Trails, **32**
Stars
    Bernard's, 127
    brightest 16, **137**
    Catalogs, **130**
    Cepheids, **207**
    Classification, **128**
    Death, **137**
    double, 131
    Fuel of, **123**
    Multiple Systems, **131**
    Names, **130**
    Neutron, **139**
    Nurseries, **124**
    Population class, **130**
    Stuff of, **141**
    Trails, **32**
    twinkle, 39
Steady State theory, 211
Stellar Nurseries, **124**
Stellar Population, **130**
Stofler, 78

strong nuclear force, 22
Sun, **93**
Sunspots, **95**
Supernova, 139
   Remnant, **150**
symmetry, 11

T

Taurus, **181**
Telescope
   aerial, 51
   Buying, **54**
   Cassegrain, 53
   Mounts, **55**
   Reflecting, 8, **52**
   Refracting, **50**
Telescopic Moon, **75**
Tesla, 223
Third Rock, **27**
Thuban, 2, 34
Tides, **71**
time, relative, 23
Tirion, 50
Tombaugh, 118
torsion balance, 20
Trapezium, 126
Twinkling Stars, **39**
Two Answers, **219**
Tycho Brahe, **4**
Tychonic system, 5

U

UFO, **219**
umbra, 79

Universe
   Expanding, **209**
Uranus, **115**
Ursa Major, **161**
Ursa Minor, **165**

V

Van Allen, 43
Variable Stars, **134**
Venus, **102**
Vesta, 107
Von Braun, 89, 232
Voyager, **122**

W

weak nuclear force, 22
Websites, Astronomy, **242**
Weirdness, **25**
Werner, 77
Whewell, 105
White, 85
Wilson, 214
Worlds Collide, **206**
Wow! signal, 224

Y

Year, **30**
Yerkes, 58

Z

Zodiac, 35, 97
Zwicky, 216

CPSIA information can be obtained
at www.ICGtesting.com
Printed in the USA
BVHW092152140922
646929BV00003B/10